THINK YOURSELF WELL

THE AMAZING POWER
OF YOUR MIND

Researched and written by
Bernard Ward

IMPORTANT: This book is intended as a reference volume only, not as a medical manual. Be sure to consult your physician before beginning any therapeutic program.

CONTENTS

HEAL YOURSELF!   7

RELAXATION
Healing from the Inside   10

MEDITATION
Simple – and Soothing   21

VISUALIZATION
Use Your Imagination   31

HYPNOSIS
Our Minds are Like Computers   39

PRAYER
The Oldest Mind Power of All   47

DREAMS
Messages from the Subconscious   58

INNER GUIDES
A Warm and Loving Friend   67

PAST LIVES
Clues that Can Make You Well   75

HUMOR
Laughter is the Best Medicine   81

BIOFEEDBACK AND MORE
More Super Healing Tips   89

HEAL YOURSELF!

This book is about power – the incredible power of the mind to heal. The power of the mind is not some mysterious, psychic phenomenon or superstitious folklore. The power of the mind – all the powers of the mind – starts with one basic idea: You control your thoughts, and with your thoughts, you can take charge of your own health and healing.

And the greatest power of all is that if you don't like your thoughts, if they're not working to make you a healthier, happier person, then you have the power to change them.

In *Think Yourself Well*, we will show you how to tap into the marvelous abilities we all have to change our thoughts and thus banish the blues, create a richer, fuller life, and heal and prevent serious, life-threatening illnesses.

For centuries, people believed in and practiced the healing powers of the mind. But with the consuming fascination with modern science, many of those natural abilities quickly fell into disfavor and were forgotten. Now, worldwide, an exciting reawakening is underway that is restoring those ancient powers to their rightful role in the process of healing.

Dr. Joan Borysenko, co-founder and director of the Mind/Body Clinic and author of *Minding the Body, Mending the Mind*, declares: "We are entering a new level in the scientific understanding of mechanisms by which faith, belief and imagination can actually unlock the mysteries of healing."

Major hospitals that once scoffed at such a view are now routinely including programs that employ mind-body techniques to help patients get well; medical centers offer classes in guided imagery techniques; doctors preach the value of meditation, prayer and faith; psychiatrists are studying past-life regression to root out the causes of present-day illnesses, and scientific researchers are proving that mind powers are real and can help people suffering from everything from migraine headaches to heart disease and life-threatening cancer.

Institutions such as The Mind/Body Medical Institute (established by the Harvard Medical School and the New England Deaconess Hospital), the Center for Positive Living and the new Office for the Study of Unconventional Medical Practices at the National Institutes of Health have virtually overnight made the powers of the mind an accepted part of the healing process.

Elsewhere, Dr. Carl Simonton, who pioneered the use of guided imagery for cancer patients, runs the Simonton Cancer Center in Pacific Palisades, CA, where thousands of patients have successfully beaten back the dreaded disease.

Dr. Dean Ornish of the University of California at San Francisco advocates the use of meditation and relaxation to reverse the effects of heart disease. He reports that such approaches could cut in half the estimated $12 billion spent on bypass surgery in one year alone.

Dr. Karen Olness, head of the Rainbow Babies and Children's Hospital in Cleveland, uses mind-over-matter techniques for children with hemophilia to help them control their bleeding.

Bernie Siegel, M.D., shocked the medical establishment with his book *Love, Medicine & Miracles,* which told how patients with cancer could use the power of their minds to help heal themselves. The book remained at the top of the best-seller list for months as millions of people embraced Dr. Siegel's beliefs. Then, one of America's most respected journalists, Bill Moyers, investigated the mind-body links in the popular PBS television program *Healing and the Mind*.

In preparing the five-part series, Moyers learned that our ancestors, from ancient philosophers to our own grandmothers, knew for centuries that emotions influenced health.

"Why," asked Moyers, "did they believe that intangibles like hope and joy and purpose could heal the body? Today's scientific researchers are asking that question, and many of them believe that what they are discovering may be leading us into a new future of medicine, one that draws from the best of both worlds: modern science and ancient wisdom."

On the following pages we will describe this "future of medicine" based on the latest information gathered from hundreds of leading researchers, specialists, clinics, hospitals, case histories, medical books and scientific reports.

Included are tips on using relaxation, meditation, guided imagery, hypnosis, prayer, humor and dream messages to heal yourself. Some of the techniques overlap and at times work together, such as relaxation/meditation/visualization, for example, or hypnosis/past-life therapy.

Of course, what works for one person might not work for another. So the key to using *Think Yourself Well* is this: Be flexible and be patient. Overnight results are possible, but don't be discouraged if it takes longer. Find the method of mind power that works best for you.

Think Yourself Well is a valuable addition to your home library. It could change your life. It could even save it.

Healing from the Inside

We begin with relaxation because almost every mind-body technique that follows rests on this process and its astonishing capacity to calm the body, quiet the mind and open channels through which the healing process can flow.

Recent research shows that relaxation makes people less susceptible to viruses. Patients suffering from chronic, unbearable pain improve dramatically when they learn relaxation techniques, while people with asthma breathe better and diabetics can reduce their need for insulin.

Relaxation has great benefits for cardiac patients. Dr. Dean Ornish, director of the Preventive Medicine Research Institute in San Francisco, studied how lifestyle changes affected heart disease. He found that relaxation training, a lifestyle change, helps lower cholesterol levels and improves blood flow to the heart.

Relaxation, Dr. Ornish points out, heals from within. Expensive bypass operations may only bypass the lifestyle problems that are causing the trouble without healing them.

Dr. Herbert Benson was the first modern researcher to demonstrate the value of relaxation in treating and healing a host of human ailments. His books, *The Relaxation Response*, *Beyond the Relaxation Response*, *The Mind/Body Effect* and *The Wellness Book*, have sold millions of copies.

As a professor of medicine at Harvard Medical School and president of Mind/Body Medical Institute, Dr. Benson has taught his relaxation technique to hundreds of thousands of stressed-out, sometimes critically ill, patients.

> **Patients who are taught how to relax are able to manage the side effects of kidney dialysis and cancer chemotherapy. Others gain an astonishing degree of power over such ailments as emphysema, skin disorders, ulcers and other stomach problems.**

RELAXATION

LEARN THESE SEVEN BASIC STEPS

1. Find a quiet place without distractions such as television, phones and street noise.

2. Choose a word or phrase to focus on. Dr. Benson recommends the word 'one', although it's best to pick something that has special meaning to you. Many people use a prayer word; others, nothing more than a soothing sound. Whatever it is, stay with that word or sound once you pick it. After awhile, it automatically triggers the relaxation response.

3. Sit upright in a comfortable position, with your hands resting naturally on your lap.

4. Let your eyes close gently. Take a few deep breaths to relax your muscles and quiet your mind.

5. Next, breathe normally, but become aware of each breath and of the slow, natural rhythm of your breathing. Repeat your focus word or your sound silently on every exhale.

6. A variety of thoughts, imagery and feelings may come to mind, but don't let them distract you. Be passive and let those thoughts go without dwelling on them. "A passive attitude appears to be the most essential factor in eliciting the relaxation response," Dr. Benson advises.

7. Continue for 10 to 20 minutes. When it's time to stop, stay quiet, with your eyes closed, for a few minutes. Let yourself slowly become fully awake and alert.

Benson says that the best results occur if patients practice the method twice a day for 10 to 20 minutes per session, but, he cautions, be flexible. Trying hard to stick to a strict routine makes you tense and defeats the whole idea of relaxing.

Dr. Karen Olness, professor of pediatrics at Case Western Reserve University, is among the many researchers who have taught Benson's relaxation techniques to their patients – with sometimes amazing results.

One hemophiliac youngster under Dr. Olness' guidance stopped his bleeding by visualizing tiny airplanes zoom-

RELAXATION

ing through his veins and dropping clotting bombs on his bleeding sites.

Dr. Olness also teaches patients how to 'think away' even the crippling pain of migraine headaches, arthritis and cancer – something that she practices as well as preaches. Dr. Olness says she once endured a long operation to fix a torn ligament in her hand using only relaxation and positive visualization as anesthesia.

MILLIONS USE 'PROGRESSIVE' RELAXATION

Dr. Edmund Jacobson, a Harvard-trained psychiatrist, developed another relaxation method nearly 80 years ago after noticing that people under stress tensed their muscles – and tense muscles aggravated the stress. He perfected 'progressive relaxation' to break that cycle. Millions of people have used it since with amazing results.

Progressive relaxation techniques are used today to treat such disorders as headaches, ulcers, high blood pressure and colitis.

Here is one variation of the technique that you can easily master to considerably speed your own healing:

First, get comfortable. Sit upright with your hands resting in your lap. You can also lie down with your feet braced lightly against a wall or heavy piece of furniture.

Close your eyes. Now make a tight fist with your right hand and tense the muscles in your wrist and forearm. Hold for about five seconds while noticing the tension you create. Unclench your fist and release the tension from your forearm, wrist and fingers. Observe how different your arm feels now compared to when it was tense. Repeat the process and then do the same thing with your left fist and forearm.

Next, tense your upper arms and shoulders. Hold for a few seconds and relax. Each time, notice the difference between how your muscles feel when tense and how they feel when relaxed.

Tense your neck – For most people, this is the tensest part of the body to begin with. Hold for a few seconds. Relax. By now, you should begin to notice a considerable

RELAXATION

difference in how much more relaxed your upper body is feeling compared to before you started.

Make a frown. In fact, scowl as hard as you can, then relax those facial muscles. Feel how the tension drains out of your face and cheeks when you let go of it.

Now push up on your toes. If you're lying down, push against the wall, or whatever it takes to create tension in your legs. Hold for a few seconds, then relax. Repeat a couple of times and you should be feeling an overall calmness and sense of peace.

During the progressive relaxation, keep your breathing normal and rhythmic. When you're finished, take a deep breath and hold it so that you feel the tension in your chest. Exhale. Inhale again and hold. Repeat this breathing exercise a few times. Each time you exhale fully, give yourself a silent affirmation such as, "I am calm" or "I am relaxed."

Finally, count to four slowly and become more alert with each count. At four, open your eyes. You will be amazed at how relaxed and refreshed you feel.

The basic principle of progressive relaxation is that by deliberately relaxing all of our muscles, group by group, we can rid ourselves of tension. The buildup of tension in our neck and head muscles is probably the most obvious and is responsible for most everyday headaches. Therefore, progressive relaxation that focuses on those muscles is often a very effective anti-headache treatment.

It's just as effective with much more serious illnesses and pain. For example, Dr. Carl Simonton urged his cancer patients to learn progressive relaxation combined with mental imagery to deal with their discomfort and the side effects of chemotherapy.

In *Getting Well Again*, Dr. Simonton recommended using the combined relaxation/mental imagery activity three times a day for 10 to 15 minutes per session.

Most people feel relaxed the first time they use this technique. But since relaxation is something that can be learned and improved upon, you will find that you'll enter into increasingly relaxed states as the process is repeated.

RELAXATION

Dr. Simonton adapted the progressive-relaxation formula to suit his patients and recorded the instructions on a cassette tape.

People at home can follow the same steps, either by having someone read the instructions or by recording their own tape. Dr. Simonton has some suggestions:

DO-IT-YOURSELF TECHNIQUE

1. Go to a quiet, softly lit room. Shut the door and sit in a comfortable chair, feet flat on the floor, eyes closed.

2. Become aware of your breathing.

3. Take in a few deep breaths, and as you let out each breath, mentally say the word, "Relax."

4. Concentrate on your face and feel any tension in your face and eyes. Make a mental picture of this tension – it might be a rope tied in a knot or a clenched fist – and then mentally picture it relaxing and becoming comfortable, like a limp rubber band.

5. Experience your face and eyes becoming relaxed. As they do so, feel a wave of relaxation spreading through your body.

6. Tense your eyes and face, squeezing tightly, then relax them and feel the relaxation spreading throughout your body. Next, apply the previous instructions to other parts of your body.

7. Move slowly down your body – jaw, neck, shoulders, back, upper and lower arms, hands, chest, abdomen, thighs, calves, ankles, feet, toes – until every part of you is relaxed. For each part of the body, mentally picture the tension. Picture the tension melting away, tense the area, then relax it.

8. When you have relaxed each part of the body, rest quietly in this comfortable state for two to five minutes.

9. Then let the muscles in your eyelids lighten up, get ready to open your eyes and become aware of the room.

10. Now let your eyes open. You are ready to go on with your usual activities.

"We use this technique pri-

RELAXATION

marily as a prelude to mental imagery, because the physical relaxation reduces tension that could distract from concentrating on the mental imagery," Dr. Simonton explained.

"The relaxation technique is also a prelude to mental imagery in another sense: Learning to use mental guidance to produce physical relaxation should help strengthen your belief that you can use your mind in support of your body."

By practicing progressive relaxation, you'll become more aware of your body and be able to pinpoint where the tension is most likely to occur. And in progressive relaxation, practice does make perfect. You'll find that after awhile you can reach the same high level of relaxation in five minutes that it took 20 minutes to achieve when you started.

Even more important, progressive relaxation is the vital first step to other mind-body methods such as guided imagery, visualization or dream work, in which the power of healing is most dramatic. Research shows that the subconscious mind is most receptive to change – and healing is most likely to take place – when the body is fully relaxed.

LULL YOUR BODY INTO RELAXATION

Autogenic training is another potent way to relax, in which you give hypnotic-like suggestions to different parts of your body by telling it to relax – and, incredibly, having it respond to your commands. Like all other relaxation techniques, autogenic training can be very effective in calming the mind and body.

> **Most people master these techniques in a matter of minutes by concentrating on feelings of heaviness and warmth throughout their bodies.**

Autogenic (which means 'self-regulating' or 'self-generating') suggestions really do make 'heavy' muscles relax and increase circulation to 'warm' areas – which usually are the necessarily first steps that lead to healing.

Sometimes, autogenic training is called *hypnotic body talking*, which means that while in a relaxed state, you verbal-

RELAXATION

ly give your body instructions on what you want it to accomplish in the way of stress reduction or healing.

Dr. Martin Shaffer is a clinical psychologist who uses autogenic training at his Stress Management Institute in San Francisco. He outlined an easy-to-follow guide to the process in his book *Life After Stress*.

You begin the same way as with any other relaxation technique – quiet room, lights down low, loose clothing, comfortable chair. Some people prefer lying on the floor with a pillow under their heads, arms at their sides, but not touching their body.

Close your eyes, take a few deep breaths and begin breathing evenly. Then, according to Dr. Shaffer, start giving your body the following instructions, one command each time you exhale:

1. My hands and arms are heavy and warm (five times).

2. My feet and legs are heavy and warm (five times).

3. My abdomen is warm and comfortable (five times). Omit this step if you have ulcers.

4. My breathing is deep and even (10 times).

5. My heartbeat is slightly calm and regular (10 times).

6. My forehead is cool (five times).

7. When I open my eyes, I will remain relaxed and refreshed (three times).

When you do open your eyes, first, slowly move your arms, hands, legs and feet for a minute or two and then rotate your head before sitting up.

All this should be done with an attitude of passive concentration. That is, observe what's happening to your body, but don't consciously try to analyze it. By all means don't criticize yourself for having distracting thoughts. If your mind wanders, simply bring it back to your instructions as soon as possible.

Another recognized leader in the new field of mind-body healing is Dr. Stephen Locke. In his book *The Healer Within: The New Medicine of Mind and Body*, Dr. Locke also described how autogenic training can play a major role when people decide to take control of their own healing process.

Autogenic training, Dr. Locke

RELAXATION

explains, is a form of self-hypnosis that relies on a repetition of verbal cues or instructions to the body that are intended to produce changes.

The person doesn't direct the changes, but simply lets the body respond to them. For example, those repetitive instructions might include: *"My right arm is heavy." "My left leg is warm."*

"My heartbeat is strong and regular." Or *"My forehead is cool."*

The Importance of Proper Breathing

As you explore autogenic training or any of the other mind-body methods of healing, you'll find that nearly all of them emphasize breathing as one of the most important ingredients in the process. This is especially true if you're using such techniques as relaxation, meditation and visualization.

In fact, proper breathing alone can produce an enormous calming and relaxing effect. The only problem is that many of us have forgotten how to breathe properly – or have never learned.

Infants breathe naturally when they sleep – not from their upper chests as most adults do, but from their diaphragms, or way down in their tummies.

As we grow older, we learn to hold in our stomachs because we think it looks better and compensate by shifting our breathing to our chest. But that's unnatural and a bad habit. Most experts in mind-body research say that by breaking that bad habit we pave the way for our own self-healing.

Psychologist Phil Nuernberger, author of *Freedom from Stress*, says that many stress-related, modern ailments are caused by improper breathing.

"The way we breathe has a profound effect on the way we feel," he says. "Fortunately, many complaints can be reversed simply by learning to breathe properly."

For example, one study suggests that chest breathers may be more susceptible to heart attacks than people who relearn to breathe from their diaphragms. Almost all of the 153 heart attack patients in the study conducted at Methodist Hospital in Minneapolis were primarily chest breathers.

Diaphragmatic breathing is not only the gateway to deep healing meditations, for in-

RELAXATION

stance, but actually increases the level of endorphins, or the natural morphine-like, painkilling chemical our bodies produce.

Many doctors now encourage their patients to practice diaphragmatic breathing techniques before they undergo surgery. Usually, these patients experience less post-operative pain, require less medication, have fewer complications and recover faster.

Here are some deep-breathing techniques that experts recommend:

● Wear loose clothes that don't bind your midsection. Get comfortable, sitting or lying down, but either way keep your back as straight as possible.

● Begin by breathing in slowly and evenly through your nostrils. At first, rest your fingertips lightly on your abdomen and feel how it expands. Do the same with your rib cage and your chest. Reverse the process when you exhale. Remember to breathe through your nostrils slowly and evenly. Gently contract the abdomen to exhale all the stale air.

Don't strain or try to force yourself into a different style of breathing too quickly. Also, don't try to over breathe and force air into your lungs. Stick to an easy rhythm. At first, try to keep your inhalation and exhalation the same length. It might help to mentally count to three slowly on each inhale and again on each exhale. As your breathing capacity increases, work up to a longer count.

To make sure you're breathing with your diaphragm and not your chest, one expert suggests that you make believe you are blowing up a balloon in your stomach. Another advises to keep your mouth closed, your tongue on the roof of your mouth and don't clench your jaw.

Another trick to try is exhaling slower than inhaling. A two-for-one system helps achieve this rhythm. Make the exhalation twice as long as the inhalation.

Breathe Like the Ocean Waves

Psychologist Beata Jencks recommends trying a whimsical exercise that she describes as "breathing through your fingertips," one of the breathing techniques described in her book *Your Body: Biofeedback at Its Best*.

RELAXATION

"Imagine inhaling through your fingertips," Dr. Jencks writes, "up the arms, into the shoulders, and then exhaling down the trunk into the abdomen and legs and leisurely throughout the toes. Repeat, and feel how this slow, deep breathing affects the whole body, the abdomen, the flanks and the chest. Do not move the shoulders."

To inhale deeply, Dr. Jencks continues, imagine you are smelling the fragrance of the first flower in spring, or visualize that your breathing is like the rising, falling motion of the ocean waves.

Learn the 'Three-Part' Breath

Breathing is one of the body's functions we can control and use as a powerful ally in our healing. Anyone who has ever been exposed to any yoga training is taught conscious breathing as one of the very first lessons.

For example, a deep-breathing technique used in conjunction with mind-body healing is something called the 'three-part breath', or the 'yogi complete breath'.

Begin as usual by expanding the abdomen, but then continue to inhale, until your midchest and upper chest areas expand. (If your collarbones lift of their own accord, you're inhaling fully.) Continue until your lungs are full. Then, as you exhale, reverse the process so that you feel as if you're deflating from top to bottom.

Slow Down and Focus on Each Breath

As you start to inhale – slowly and smoothly through your nostrils – say "one" to yourself silently. When your lungs are completely filled, pause and mentally say "relax" and then begin exhaling. Make each exhale at least three seconds or longer.

When you've exhaled entirely, pause again and say "two." Now repeat the process. The normal breathing rate is 16-18 per minute. But in your practice sessions set a goal of about 10-14 breaths per minute. This conscious effort to slow your breathing soon becomes automatic and makes access to complete relaxation – and the mind-body healing that follows – much easier and quicker.

MEDITATION

Simple — and Soothing

Meditation as a healing tool is not some mysterious, complicated ritual that only religious mystics or saints can employ after years of concentration and practice.

Meditation is the simplest thing in the world. In fact, to some degree we all meditate every day at those times when our attention becomes focused on something – a sound, a picture, a memory – and our minds float free, clearing any thoughts about what has happened or might happen.

However, there is an enormous difference between those somewhat casual meditations and meditation that is directed toward the goal of healing, what some teachers term 'mindfulness meditation'. But, hold on! Don't let that scare you off. Meditation is still easier than you might think, and it offers a true multitude of blessings.

In his best seller *Love, Medicine & Miracles*, Dr. Bernie Siegel writes about some of those blessings: "The physical benefits of meditation have recently been well-documented by Western medical researchers, notably Dr. Herbert Benson. It tends to lower or normalize blood pressure, pulse rate and the levels of stress hormones in the blood.

> "Meditation also raises the pain threshold and reduces one's biological age. Its benefits are multiplied when combined with regular exercise. In short, it reduces wear and tear on both body and mind, helping people live better and longer."

"The spiritual healing that occurs with meditation is at least as important as the physiological benefits, though more difficult to describe. Everybody's experience of it is different, ranging from general feelings of peacefulness to very specific insights into the dilemmas of individual lives."

Now, more than ever before, cases in which meditation has been a major factor in quite incredible recoveries from major illnesses are being carefully documented by statisticians at top hospitals and research centers throughout the world.

A 39-year-old woman stunned researchers at the University of Arkansas College of Medicine by demonstrating that she could depress her immune response on command. Her secret? A nine-year history of meditation.

To test her ability, doctors twice gave the woman injections of the virus that causes chicken pox and shingles. The first time, her body reacted to the virus by turning red where she was injected and her white blood cells increased, in an absolutely normal way, to fight off the invader. However, when she inhibited her response while meditating, the white blood cell count dropped sharply and the skin reaction to the injection was significantly less.

Researchers are now investigating if that phenomenal ability might work in reverse – meditation to boost the immune system, which is the major target of the AIDS virus.

Elsewhere, a woman in her mid-40s began attending the meditation classes offered at

MEDITATION

Boston's Mind/Body Clinic. Her purpose was to find relief from the allergies that had tormented her all her life. They were so severe that she often had to stay in bed. The meditation techniques she learned proved highly successful in helping control the allergy attacks, report doctors.

Later, the same woman was in a car accident that left her with a crushed chest and brain damage. Doctors said her chances of surviving were about one percent. But the woman beat the overwhelming odds, although, like a stroke victim, she had to relearn how to walk and talk. To do so, she relied on the powers of concentration she had learned in meditation class to make an astonishing recovery.

"From personal experience," writes Dr. Siegel, "I know that these healing intervals can take many forms... Ainslie Meares, an Australian doctor who specializes in a kind of intensive meditation work done with groups of cancer patients, described what he saw as the ultimate aim of meditation.

"'Not only is there a reduction in the level of anxiety, and in some cases a regres-

UNDERSTANDING LIFE AND DEATH

sion of the cancer, but patients take away from these sessions a nonverbal understanding of many things, including, most importantly, life and death. It is a genuine understanding...that life and death are simply different facets of an underlying process.'

"...Meares attributed this understanding of the 'mysteries of life' to the particular kind of meditation he had his patients do... When Meares talked about the spiritual growth he had witnessed in his patients, he was talking about what he called the 'onflow', that is, the way in which the results of meditation spill over into one's life."

Most methods of meditating start by having you assume a relaxed and upright sitting position, neither too rigid nor too relaxed. Sitting in the cross-legged lotus position of yoga is not necessary unless that's your preference. A straight-backed chair or meditation bench will do. But lying down is not a good idea, since meditation will put you in such

MEDITATION

a relaxed state you might fall asleep and, ideally, the technique should leave you alert, energized and focused.

Try to set aside a certain time to practice every day. Early in the morning when you first get up and just before retiring at night are often ideal times to meditate.

There are countless methods of meditating, some more complicated and intense than others. You need to find the method that suits you best, but remember that all methods have one thing in common: They are gateways to the healing powers of the mind. Meditation moves us into an altered state in which we can utilize the limitless knowledge and astonishing powers locked in our unconscious mind.

For many in need of healing, there are gentle comforting guides waiting beyond those gates to take your hand and help you on your wonderful, restful journey through meditation.

For example, in his essay *The Practice of Meditation*, Alan Watts writes that meditation "is the art of being completely centered in the here and now" and then offers some basic tips anyone can use to meditate:

"Simply sit down, close your eyes and listen to all sounds that may be going on – without trying to name or identify them. Listen as you would listen to music. If you find that verbal thinking will not drop away, don't attempt to stop it by force of willpower. Just keep your tongue relaxed, floating easily in the lower jaw, and listen to your thoughts as if they were birds chattering outside – mere noise in the skull. They will eventually subside on their own, as a turbulent and muddy pool will become calm and clear if left alone.

> 'BECOME AWARE OF YOUR BREATHING...'

"Allow your lungs to work in whatever rhythm seems congenial to them. And for a while just sit, listening and feeling your breath. But, if possible, don't call it that. Simply experience the nonverbal happening. You may object that this is not 'spiritual' meditation but mere attention to the 'physical' world, but it should be understood that

MEDITATION

the spiritual and the physical are only ideas, philosophical conceptions, and that the reality of which you are now aware is not an idea. Furthermore, there is no 'you' aware of it. That was also just an idea. Can you hear yourself listening?"

> The initial purpose of meditation is to focus your attention on the present moment and to discover the miraculous power that dwells within us – not in the past, not in the future, but right now. As Jane Roberts stressed in *The Seth Materials,* "the point of power is in the present."

To keep attention focused on the present, many teachers suggest starting by concentrating on one simple object or another. Your own breathing is the most common method of focusing attention in meditation. Some methods require the use of words, phrases, repetitive sounds, or even mental images. External objects such as a candle flame also work – anything that helps you refocus your attention if it wanders.

Regular practice, rather than when or how long you meditate, is important. When meditation becomes part of their daily routine, most people find that the mind powers they develop while meditating carry over into their everyday lives – and that's where the healing power comes in.

Every week, men and women in search of healing gather to meditate at the Mind/Body clinic. Almost every ailment imaginable is represented – cancer, heart disease, arthritis, hypertension, migraine headaches, diabetes and multiple sclerosis among others.

All those people attend, says Dr. Joan Borysenko, "to learn how to use their mind as a tool." Dr. Borysenko is co-founder of the clinic, a service of the New England Deaconess Hospital and Harvard Medical School. A cell biology researcher and trained psychologist, Dr. Borysenko also is author of *Minding the Body, Mending the Mind*. She is now president of Mind/Body Health Sciences, Inc.

MEDITATION

'MINDFULNESS MEDITATION'

This method taught at the clinic helps people gain more control over their own destinies and direct their own healing. The meditation process is summed up in eight, easy-to-follow steps:

1. Choose a quiet spot where you will not be disturbed by other people or by the telephone. This extends to pets, as well. You must make time for yourself. This is your time that you take for yourself to more fully understand the interaction of your mind, body and spirit.

2. Sit in a comfortable position, with back straight and arms and legs uncrossed, unless you choose to sit cross-legged on a cushion.

3. Close your eyes. This makes it much easier to concentrate.

4. Relax your muscles, starting with your scalp and working down to the tips of your toes. Become aware of each part of your body in succession, letting go as much as you can each time you exhale. Inhale deeply and notice how your body relaxes as you let go. Let your shoulders slump lower with each exhale to enhance the sense of letting go of the burdens of the outer world that are weighing you down.

Starting with your forehead, become aware of tension to some degree as you breathe in – and then let go of any obvious tension as you breathe out. Go through the rest of your body in this way, proceeding down through your eyes, jaw, neck, shoulders, arms, hands, chest, upper back, middle back and midriff, lower back, belly, pelvis, buttocks, thighs, calves and feet. This need only take a minute or two.

5. Become aware of your breathing, noticing how the breath goes in and out, without trying to control it in any way. You are breathing all the time, aware of it or not. Let the breathing happen by itself. You'll probably notice that your breathing gets slower and shallower as the meditation progresses. That's the relaxation response taking over and slowing things down.

MEDITATION

6. **Choose a word or a sound to focus on,** and repeat it silently in time with your breathing.

7. **Don't think about the 'right' way to meditate.** If you're worrying about whether you're doing it right, then you're not meditating. But don't be critical of yourself. Just take note of your tendency to judge yourself, then let it go, and shift your focus back to your breathing. Most people discover how difficult it is to keep their mind from wandering during meditation. Don't try to stop it, but when your mind does wander, gently bring it back to concentrating on breathing and focusing.

8. **Practice at least once a day** for 10 to 20 minutes. Meditation becomes easier, deeper and more peaceful after repeated practice.

Another method of healing meditation is that outlined by Roy Eugene Davis in his *Easy Guide to Meditation*. Davis, who conducts meditation seminars all over North America, calls meditation "the simple process of directing attention to the source of energy and creativity which resides at the center of our innermost being."

In his *Easy Guide*, Davis offers several tips for beginning meditators: Select a time when

> **If you can sit twice a day for 10 to 20 minutes, so much the better. The preferred times are early morning, after a shower and exercise (if you exercise), but before breakfast, or before dinner. The worst times are when you're tired. Meditation is a concentration exercise, and if you're tired, you'll fall asleep. After a heavy meal, most people feel sluggish.**

you are not too tired, as well as a comfortable place for meditating where you won't be disturbed for at least 20 minutes while you're learning and practicing.

Loosen any tight articles of clothing so that you can relax fully. Sit upright in a comfortable chair. The ideal meditation posture is one in which you can sit for the duration of med-

MEDITATION

itation without having to move the body unnecessarily.

Close your eyes and, for a few minutes, just get used to the sound of silence. Notice how your body reacts when you inhale and exhale. Don't try to change your breathing, just observe it. Let the body inhale and exhale naturally. Continue this process for about 20 minutes.

> Your attention is bound to wander during these early sessions. Don't get upset with yourself when it does. Just gently bring your attention back to your breathing process and feel the breath flowing in and out of you.
>
> At the end of the session, remain seated for a few minutes with your eyes closed. Feel the relaxation that flows through you and enjoy that sense of contentment. Let the peace of meditation fill your mind and body.

Don't struggle to concentrate on thoughts or feelings. Non-effort is the key to success. All that is required is that you be gentle with yourself.

At the end of the session, remain seated for a few minutes with your eyes closed. Feel the relaxation that flows through you and enjoy that sense of contentment. Let the peace of meditation fill your mind and body.

For a slightly more involved meditation process, try repeating silently to yourself some word of your choosing. Focus your attention on the sound of the word as you exhale rather than on the breathing process.

Practice on a regular schedule, preferably twice a day, for at least six weeks. With regular practice, you'll soon notice that your powers of concentration have increased, almost without effort, and that you look forward to meditation periods for the sense of relaxation and revitalization you're left with after each session.

However, Davis cautions, don't look for something dramatic to happen while meditating at first. It's better to expect nothing. Just keep practicing on a regular basis and whatever unfolds will fulfill your personal needs. Medita-

MEDITATION

tion is the time to consciously free your mind of any concerns about problems or illnesses.

Rest for a few minutes after the session ends and simply allow the meditation experience to settle into your mind and body.

PRACTICE, PRACTICE

If healing is the goal, then rest in the stillness following meditation practice and know that an inner intelligence, or spiritual guide, if you prefer, has got the message and knows what needs to be done to fix the problem.

Let your attention flow to the area of the body where the healing is needed. Visualize and feel that the condition is disappearing and that perfect health is taking its place.

End the session with a feeling of gratitude and a small prayer or simple word of thanksgiving.

"This meditation process is suitable for anyone, even a person with no religious inclinations," Davis explains. "With a release of stress, one will notice a general improvement in health, peace of mind and sharper mental abilities. If healing is your goal, remember that consciousness is superior to mind, and mind is superior to body – and that healing begins first in your consciousness, then is reflected through the mind to the body."

Here's another basic method for meditating that anyone can start with.

Most beginners find the most difficult part of meditating is quieting the mind. If this is your problem, start with a 10-minute practice session and work up to about 20 minutes gradually.

Find a comfortable chair or place to sit on the floor. Take off your shoes and loosen any tight clothing. If you are feeling tense, try rolling your neck and shrugging your shoulders a few times. When you feel ready, close your eyes and let your hands rest in your lap.

Take three deep breaths. Inhale and exhale deeply and slowly and let your mind become quieter with each breath. Some silent affirmation or brief prayer might help to clear your mind of all the chatter at this point, something like, "I now choose to enjoy the stillness."

29

MEDITATION

Continue taking slow, deep breaths, only now begin to focus your attention on this breath. Feel it flowing through your nostrils, deep into your abdomen and back out. Some people find it helps to count: 'one' when you inhale; 'two' when you exhale, and so on up to 10. Then start over again with number one when you inhale and begin to let the silent sound of the numbers fill your mind.

Use these silent, rhythmic counts to refocus your attention when your attention wanders. Gradually, as you become more and more comfortable with the count, you'll discover a remarkable new awareness of your body.

Use this basic meditation technique as a starting point in your recovery. Meditation teachers experienced in the healing process, or mind-body specialists who now practice in most major medical facilities, can guide you into deep meditations where you can truly unlock the fantastic healing powers of the mind. You'll be glad you did.

> **If you are in need of healing, this is the time to slowly shift your attention to that specific area of your body that is the problem. Imagine that you are inhaling a healing potion and directing it to flow through the troubled area. Imagine that the breath you exhale is carrying away the disease.**

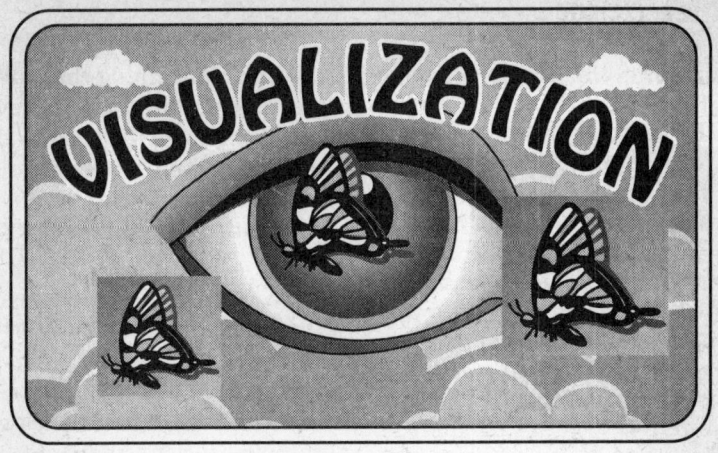

VISUALIZATION

Use Your Imagination

Visualization and guided imagery are a lot alike: They are two of the mightiest of all the healing powers of the mind. And each one takes only one thing to make it work – the astonishing creative ability of your imagination.

Using visualization or imagery, you heal yourself by building strong pictures in your mind of what you want to happen and then believing that those mind pictures are real. The secret to building positive images in your mind is to visualize precise details. Imagine how something looks, sounds, smells, feels and tastes.

In other words, imagine something that seems so real that you trick your body into believing it is real.

The potential healing power of visualization and imagery is staggering.

Alan Cohen, writing in *Setting the Seen: Creative Visualization for Healing,* said: "There is a creative power in the mind that offers unlimited possibilities to all of us. The potential has been virtually unused... The essence of the power of creative visual-

VISUALIZATION

ization is this simple formula: SEE WHAT YOU WANT TO BE!"

According to David Bresler, Ph.D., co-director of the Academy of Guided Imagery in Mill Valley, CA, and author of *Free Yourself from Pain*, pain-control imagery is the key to coping until the cause of the pain can be resolved. "It's a way of using your mind to mobilize your body's healing forces," he says.

In the past decade, imagery and visualization have become key elements in the treatment of numerous illnesses including cancer, heart disorders and diseases of the immune system. Research has documented the imagination's tremendous impact on healing, even though experts still don't know exactly how it works.

Visualization is simply the process of making mental pictures or images. You use your imagination to visualize, or create, whatever you desire. In the case of healing, that means stopping the disorder or strengthening the body's natural defenses so it can cope with the problem.

Children, says Dr. Bernie Siegel in *Peace, Love & Healing*, are great at visualizing health and imagining their illness away, because "they haven't yet made the black and white distinction between 'real' and 'imaginary' that makes visualization so hard for many adults."

Dr. Karen Olness, a professor of pediatrics at Case Western Reserve University, has achieved some amazing results teaching visualization techniques to young patients at Children's Hospital in Cleveland, including children suffering from cancer, hemophilia, arthritis, asthma and chronic pain.

> One boy with hemophilia so severe he was confined to a wheelchair most of the time learned to use his imagination to lower his pain and, in his words, "stop my bleeds." He did it by imagining he was flying a fighter plane through his body and diving into his blood vessels to drop bombs of Factor 8, the clotting substance his body needed.

BE LUKE SKYWALKER!

A nine-year-old boy was diagnosed with an inoperable and what doctors said was an incurable brain tumor. Specialists at the Menninger Foundation's Voluntary Controls Program encouraged the boy to imagine a *Star Wars* setting with the tumor as the evil invader and himself as the gallant leader in a successful space battle against the tumor.

The imagery was so effective that five months later the tumor was gone – without any other type of treatment being used.

Another astonishing success story in which visualization beat cancer is that of a woman with breast cancer.

The woman told Dr. Siegel that she "imagined small, delicate birds searching my breast for crumbs. To my surprise my imagery took the form of the cancer being golden crumbs... Each day, the birds would eat the golden crumbs. It was amazing to me that I visualized the cancer in this form, as being crumbs too golden-rich for my body. After the birds had eaten their fill, I would then imagine a pure being of intense spiritual white light entering my body. I would then pray to God for guidance, renewal and protection.

"One morning... I sat down for my meditation and visualization. The white light suddenly appeared and coursed down through my head, spreading like white heat through my breast and limbs. I felt the power take hold of me... After a short, intense interval I slumped sideways in exhaustion. I knew something extraordinary had happened."

A few days later, the woman went for a checkup. A mammogram revealed that the cancer had disappeared.

Says Dr. Siegel: "Some of the most successful kinds of visualization have been images of tumors as food being eaten by white cells disguised as Pac-Men... I suggest that patients use animated symbols. One child saw his cancer as cat food and immune cells as white pussycats. Another patient visualized birds and birdseed. One lady who had oat-cell cancer pictured mares and does eating her oats."

One businessman with throat cancer started a visualization

VISUALIZATION

> "Creative visualization is the perfect tool for healing because it goes straight to the source of the problem – your own mental concepts and images," Karen Olness says. "Begin to picture yourself, and affirm to yourself, that you are in perfect radiant health; see your problem as completely healed and cured."

program in which he imagined his disease-fighting white cells as miners with pickaxes, chopping away at the tumor and hauling it off to the dump.

His doctors discovered the tumor had shrunk to half its original size. And not only was an operation successful, but the patient left the hospital two days later – just as he had imagined.

One man began visualizing the cancer in his body as tiny creatures and his own white blood cells as heroic white knights on horseback, riding to his rescue and lancing or trampling the creatures until they were defeated. Another patient imagined the radiation he was receiving was the healing rays of the sun. A third visualized her chemotherapy as a powerful, magical potion that exploded her cancer cells the instant it touched them.

But visualization and imagery can be just as effective in healing other disorders and disabling injuries as it is with cancer or other such diseases that invade the body and attack immune systems.

IT WORKS FOR BRAIN AND SPINAL INJURIES, TOO

For example, California psychologist Dr. James Meade Jr. uses these mind-body techniques with patients who have suffered brain or spinal injuries. Incredibly, many of his patients learn to walk and talk again – by first imagining that it is happening in their minds.

Another man also relearned full coordination of his arms and legs by imagining himself skipping through a beautiful, sun-drenched field of wildflowers, catching colorful butterflies and then releasing them to fly again.

One patient who was having

VISUALIZATION

difficulty regaining his sense of balance created a visualization scene in which he saw himself as a tightrope walker whose fine-tuned sense of balance allowed him to perform amazing highwire feats. If he slipped, the man merely visualized grabbing the wire, pulling himself back up, and continuing with his act to thunderous applause from an admiring crowd.

Alan Cohen described several imaging techniques including this guided visualization, which you can tape and play back while you relax and let your imagination flow with these words:

"This image is very powerful for physical healing," Cohen wrote. "It is especially effective when done while lying in bed before going to sleep. Regular practice of this visualization for five minutes each night will greatly enhance the healing process in the body."

HERE ARE STEP-BY-STEP INSTRUCTIONS

1. **"Take three very deep breaths** and feel that you are releasing all thoughts and tensions from the day. With each in-breath, visualize clear, pure, healing energy filling your chest, and with each out-breath imagine any stress or negativity being completely expelled from your system. Do this as long as you need, until you feel that you have flushed out your system and filled yourself with light... (extended pause)...

2. **"Now inhale deeply, and as** you exhale, imagine that you are pouring healing energy down your left leg. Visualize your left leg as hollow, and as you breathe you are completely filling it with health and life. Repeat this healing breath, making sure to energize the whole leg, right down to the tips of your toes. Feel that your leg is open and porous, like a sponge, and it gladly accepts

> "People don't die from a small breast tumor since it doesn't affect any vital organs. But you can die from giving up. You can die from the workings of the imagination. And from it, you can also gain life."

VISUALIZATION

the wholeness you are channeling to it. One more time, inhale deeply, hold the breath energy in your chest for a few seconds, and then flow it down your left leg, as if you are infusing it with a perfect pattern that all of the atoms, cells and organs can form around. Feel, too, that your left leg is surrounded for a few inches with a fluffy, white light, like a substance of health energy...

3. "Now turn your attention to the right leg and breathe into it. Charge it with energy and light. Offer it three healing breaths, until it feels balanced and radiant, like the left leg... (sufficient pause)... After your third breath, experience how wonderful and alive your legs feel, as if they are brand new...

4. "When your legs are completely filled with light, give energy to your left arm. Breathe into it as if it is a sponge. As you pour sparkling light into it, it becomes fluffy and open. Breathe into it again, and see how it seems to expand more with each breath. Make sure to pour the energy into your fingers and hands, right down to the fingertips. See how fulfilled your arm becomes as you give it your loving attention in three breaths...

5. "Energize your right arm now, and see how it loosens up and has a kind of floating sensation as you breathe three times into it. Experience the wonderful strength in the right arm, and feel a healing flow of peaceful life energize it right into your fingertips. Feel, too, how flexible and alive your fingers are. It is a marvelous and peaceful feeling. You can even surround your right arm with an aura of healthy vitality, as your energy field extends beyond your physical body.

6. "Now turn your attention to the left side of your torso, breathing life into all of the organs from your shoulder to your hip. Think of the organs that live within you: your heart, your left lung, your spleen. Feel that these organs are your friends, that you can help them and make them happy by giving them your positive attention. Take a deep breath, and as you exhale fill the entire left side of your torso with healing light. Visualize all of the organs accepting this gift with gratefulness and enthusiasm. Again, breathe into the left side, this

VISUALIZATION

time filling the organs with yet deeper and more subtle energy, as if the energy from your breath could just seep deep, deep into your cells, like a healing balm that finds its way into even the smallest spaces.

7. "Finally, take one more breath and imagine that you are sending energy into the tiniest cells, and even into the very atoms of your body. Feel how wonderful and peaceful it is to be healthy and alive...

8. "Now focus on the right side of your torso, which is joyous to receive your attention. Consider the right lung, the liver and the kidneys. Now give them your loving breath. Breathe three times to the right side, at your own pace, and feel the life and love within yourself. Know that you are doing your body a great service and that the results of this attention will make themselves known to you in the form of health and happiness. Concentrate very clearly, and allow the natural healing process to work within you. Your natural state is health, and now you are rightfully claiming it.

9. "Give your attention now to your shoulders. If you have had any stress or tension in your shoulders or neck, now is your opportunity to let it go. Take a deep breath and pour your loving peace into all of the muscles in your neck. Keep breathing and imagine that two firm, yet gentle, warm hands are resting on your shoulders, and the energy from these hands is steadily and surely flowing into all the muscles in your neck, coating all the nerves with a balm of quiet restfulness. Stay with your shoulders and keep giving them gentle breaths as long as you need to let them be completely at ease.

10. "Now bring your awareness to your head. Notice if you are holding any tension or tightness here. Are you keeping your jaw tight? Are you wrinkling your forehead? Is your scalp tight? If so, now is your moment to let it all go. Very gently take a deep breath and breathe it to the left side of your face and head. Feel a soothing peacefulness rolling through your left eye, cheek and ear. This wave of ease releases any remnants of stress on this side of your head. Experience how nice and peaceful it is to be free of tension and relaxed...

VISUALIZATION

"Do the same, now, for the right side of your head. Your right cheek, eye, ear and temple are waiting for your soothing breath. Feel these parts of yourself respond as you give them what they need...

11. "Now breathe once to the front of your face. Focus especially on the eyes and the muscles that support them. Visualize the eyes resting peacefully in their perfect place, and feel the energy flowing from the brain, through the optic nerve to the eyes. Feel how smooth and soft your forehead is, like a little baby's. See your face as radiant and bright...

12. "Now breathe softly to the back of your head. There are many important glands and organs at the base of your skull, and now you can help them renew themselves and function perfectly. Feel a wonderful flow of peaceful light through the back of your head, and allow it to rest perfectly and gently just as it is.

13. "Now bring your awareness to your brain. The brain controls all the other bodily functions. As you energize the brain you heal every single cell of your body. Very gently breathe loving light into your brain, with a deep appreciation for the marvelous work that it does. Thank it for the amazing way it keeps you whole, a function far more miraculous than any human being has ever been able to comprehend. This is your moment to express your gratefulness by breathing love and peace into it. This is your moment for complete health...(extended pause)...

"Continue to breathe deeply and slowly, until your entire body rests in a happy, peaceful feeling, and you know that you are a wonderful, whole, alive person. You have now claimed and experienced the complete health that is rightfully yours."

> **Mind-body advocates urge that visualization be used as a supplement to conventional treatments such as chemotherapy and surgery, or with alternative therapies (yoga, diet, acupuncture, etc). It will speed the normal healing process amazingly.**

HYPNOSIS

Our Minds are Like Computers

Our brains do what they are programmed to do and follow the commands we give them.

Our thoughts and mental images determine how we feel and behave. If we want to change how we feel, we have to change the programming and issue new commands – just like computers.

Hypnosis and self-hypnosis – once scorned as hocus-pocus sideshow trickery – are now accepted as highly effective tools for re-programming our thoughts and thus changing our physical conditions.

A lot of myths and misunderstandings about hypnosis still exist, so many patients who could use this as a mind-body healing technique may need some help getting started and removing any lingering doubts and misconceptions – and that generally means working with a trained hypnotherapist, at least in the early stages.

Hypnotists use a variety of techniques to put patients into a relaxed state when the mind is open to suggestion. Usually, that technique involves nothing more than talking to the pa-

39

HYPNOSIS

tient in a quiet, rhythmical voice, suggesting visual images that help the patient relax deeply and completely.

> A hypnotic trance is nothing like the 'zombie' state so often depicted in movies. In hypnotism, the patient's awareness is heightened tremendously and his concentration is intensely focused. One therapist said it is a lot like being deeply absorbed in a good movie or book.

This is when the patient is most receptive to suggestions of healing. Following the guidance of the hypnotist, patients can 'imagine' pain leaving their bodies, tumors shrinking and vanishing, severe burns healing rapidly and more.

At the Minneapolis Children's Medical Center, where hypnosis is frequently used to help children cope with pain and the intense discomfort of chemotherapy, Dr. Daniel Kohen reports that "the active ingredient in hypnosis is imagery," which is why this mind-body technique works so well with children. Imagination plays a major role in their lives and they haven't yet lost the ability to pretend.

Although hypnosis was used as an anesthesia more than a century ago, it has only been within the past decade that it has become widely used to control pain and fight disease. Strangely enough, much of the new interest in hypnosis as a powerful mind-body procedure started with the common wart.

A patient afflicted with painful plantar (foot) warts sought treatment in Massachusetts General Hospital's psychosomatic medicine unit. Under hypnosis, the man was given suggestions that his warts would disappear, even though the warts were caused by a virus. But the hypnosis worked – and that led to a series of other studies on how hypnosis might be used to promote healing of much more serious medical conditions.

"We've discovered that hypnosis is very good at pain control," says Dr. Eugene E. Levitt, a professor at the Indiana University School of Medicine and a member of the American

Board of Psychological Hypnosis. "That is one of its outstanding applied uses."

Dr. Martin Orne, director of the unit for experimental psychiatry at the Institute of Pennsylvania Hospital and one of America's foremost authorities on hypnotism, says that, for many people, "hypnosis is one of the few effective ways for providing pain relief over a long period of time without risk."

For example, hypnosis is an outstanding mind-body technique for treating people who have been severely burned.

In one nightmarish case, a factory worker fell into a pool of molten aluminum. As soon as the burn victim appeared at a New Orleans hospital, Dr. Dabney Ewin, professor of surgery and psychiatry at Tulane University, was rushed in to hypnotize the patient.

With the patient in a trance, Dr. Ewin began feeding him suggestions that the badly burned leg was beginning to feel cool and comfortable. To everyone's amazement, the man recovered quicker than anyone ever imagined he could – and without serious infections, without complications and without disfiguring scars.

Dr. Ewin says that placing a patient under hypnosis within a couple of hours of the burn or injury dramatically speeds the healing process while preventing most of the pain and tissue damage.

THE POWERFUL MIND-BODY CONNECTION

Patients burned on both sides of their bodies have been asked, under hypnosis, to make the temperature of one side higher than that of the other. To raise the temperature meant they had to increase the blood flow to the burned areas using nothing but the power of their minds. Patients were able to raise their temperatures by as much as four degrees celsius, and when they did, their healing was dramatically improved.

Hypnosis is also often used today to help cancer patients deal with their pain, with the side effects of radiation and chemotherapy and to reduce their dependency on medication.

Using a method called 'creative suggestion', hypnotized patients visualize their white blood cells swarming around

HYPNOSIS

and devouring cancer cells. The result is a steady improvement in their conditions.

One study showed that even healthy people can boost their white cell count by as much as 40 percent using either hypnosis or self-hypnosis.

The results prove, said one expert, that: "The mind can influence the body by changing the biochemistry of the blood."

Added Dr. Levitt, "The evidence is clear that if you introduce hypnosis techniques in a terminal-cancer ward, you will see the demand for painkillers such as Demerol go down."

Dr. David E. Bresler, author of *Free Yourself from Pain*, described how one patient used imagery to overcome severe back pain that had disabled him for years.

Under hypnotic guidance, the patient was given suggestions to 'substitute his symptom', or mentally shift the pain in his back to another area of his body, specifically the soles of his feet.

Eventually, the patient cured himself by literally 'walking away' his pain. "He imagined the pain leaving his body and scattering on the ground as he walked along," Dr. Bresler reported.

> **In other areas, hypnosis is highly effective in dental work with patients who don't want to take painkillers. People suffering from such disorders as migraine headaches, shingles, tinnitus, arthritis and back pain find quick relief through the mind-body connection of hypnosis.**

The question asked by most people who haven't experienced this technique is: Can I be hypnotized? The answer is that most people can be, although some are more susceptible than others. A few can even reach such deep trances that they have open-heart surgery without using any other kind of anesthesia.

If you're good at imagining things and letting your imagination take over, then hypnosis probably will work very well for you. If you can believe you're relaxing in the sun on some beautiful beach while the doctor stitches up a cut on your arm, then you're an excellent subject.

HYPNOSIS

There are several basic hypnosis techniques that therapists use to help patients deal with pain. One often used is called the 'glove'. Under hypnosis, the patient is told that his or her hand is covered by a thick wool or work glove that makes it completely numb to any pain. The patient later is able to transfer that numbness to the site of the pain using symptom substitution.

In the 'fist' technique, patients picture capturing all of their pain in a fist. The tighter the fist, the more pain they can catch and hold. Once the pain they're experiencing is all in that fist, they can throw it away. The technique works so well with some patients that they can get rid of their pain for several hours at a stretch.

But can people really hypnotize themselves? Can they slip into a trance when the pain starts without the help of a hypnotist?

Hypnosis experts say the answer definitely is yes – and, in fact, self-hypnosis may be even more effective in some cases.

Regular periods of relaxation and practice by yourself, using positive imagery, is an excellent way to enhance and speed healing and recovery from physical injuries, illnesses or surgical operations.

Dr. Elmer Green, who pioneered research in biofeedback at the Menninger Foundation, once said that as we learn to put ourselves in a self-hypnotic state, "things that we visualize begin to happen with increasing frequency. Our bodies tend to do what they are told to do, if we know how to tell them and that's done by imagining and visualizing the intended change while in a relaxed state."

HOW SELF-HYPNOSIS WORKS

In self-hypnosis, the patient says the words of induction to himself, or listens to a tape of the induction he has previously recorded. Doctors say that self-hypnosis is such a great anti-pain tool because patients discover they are not helpless, which is what often makes the pain seem worse.

There are scores of books available on self-hypnosis and they all contain variations of induction procedures you can use. While the specific words or induction techniques might

HYPNOSIS

vary, most self-hypnosis books contain the same general guidelines that Bernie Zilbergeld and Arnold Lazarus covered in their book *Mind Power: Getting What You Want through Mental Training*. For example, the foundation of their 'mental training' (or self-hypnosis) is the ability to relax.

"Inducing a trance," they write, "usually involves some kind of relaxation. People help themselves to relax by taking deep breaths, by imagining peaceful scenes, by focusing on a phrase or word (as in meditation) or in a number of other ways. Anything that helps the person relax and turn inward is fine. Those who already know how to focus and relax, for instance, because of experience with meditation, biofeedback, the techniques of natural childbirth or some other relaxation method, should use the skills they possess."

Here are some of their suggestions:

1. "Make your images and suggestions as specific as possible. We ask people to imagine themselves feeling confident in a particular situation. It's fine to tell yourself that you're becoming more assertive and confident. It's even better to say that you're becoming more assertive in telling your spouse how you feel about the way he or she didn't follow through on a promise to cut the lawn.

2. "Specificity, clarity and involvement of other senses come with time and practice. If they still aren't as vivid as you want, it will probably help to practice imagining all sorts of things for a few days. For instance, look at an apple, then close your eyes and imagine the apple. Look at a car or a chair or a pen, then close your eyes and imagine it. Keep practicing like this for a while and your images will get clearer.

3. "Maintain control over your imagery. Many people have a tendency to drift off into their usual negative self-suggestion when practicing images. The tendency to do this is understandable, but it's still destructive. The way to avoid this is simple: Just refocus your attention on the positive imagery. If you keep doing this, you'll find that it becomes easier to do and that the negative fantasies either don't appear as often or don't have as much power.

HYPNOSIS

"Use words and images positively rather than negatively. For instance, tell yourself how much comfort you'll feel rather than how much pain you won't. Imagine yourself feeling comfortable, even if your goal is to be free of pain.

4. "Give yourself something to do. Don't leave a vacuum. If you tell yourself you won't smoke or won't get angry, you're not giving yourself anything to do except sit there without smoking or stand there without being angry. It's very hard to imagine yourself not doing something. Action works best, so imagine yourself doing something that reflects the feeling or state you're seeking.

5. "Use lots of repetition. Give suggestions a number of times, changing the wording slightly to add variety. You'll know you're being over-repetitive when it gets boring to listen to.

6. "Keep suggestions and images simple and concise. Don't try to pack too much into one suggestion, one image or one session. Better to err on the side of too little than too much.

7. "Recall past successes to set the right emotional tone for your mental-training session and use them in post-hypnotic suggestions.

8. "Treat yourself well in your training. Compliment and verbally reward yourself as much as possible."

Much of the healing power of self-hypnosis comes with the post-hypnotic suggestions you give yourself, so spend some time making a short list of these suggestions before you start practicing self-hypnosis.

Zilbergeld and Lazarus recommend that the suggestions be as accurate and specific as you can make them so that they really target pain reduction or whatever healing you're working on. Tell yourself how you will feel, not how you won't feel.

> **The more you repeat the post-hypnotic suggestions, the more effective they will be. Try changing the wording slightly on different repetitions, so that what you tell yourself over and over again is positive, powerful reinforcement.**

45

HYPNOSIS

Listen to the tape often – at least four or five times a day. After a week or so, you can start decreasing the amount of time you listen to the tape because you'll be repeating the suggestions to yourself without being reminded.

Countless patients have found that, in addition to pain control, self-hypnosis is a valuable tool in helping manage chronic conditions such as asthma or migraine headaches.

Doctors in San Antonio achieved some incredible results when they trained young asthma sufferers in self-hypnosis. Six of the eight youngsters involved in the project significantly reduced the severity of their symptoms within two months, and the frequency of the asthma attacks in three months. They nearly eliminated trips to hospitals for emergency room treatment and cut their medication needs to almost nothing.

The next time you have a headache, even if it isn't a migraine, sit or lie down, close your eyes and do a brief relaxation technique to quiet your mind. When you're calm and relaxed, visualize yourself enjoying a warm summer day at the beach. A cool breeze off the ocean soothes your face, while your hands and arms grow warmer as they bask in the sun.

Feel your hands getting warmer and warmer, until they're almost too hot to touch. Spend several minutes focusing on the warmth you're experiencing in this pleasant, peaceful setting. Then open your eyes. You'll probably find that while your hands are still warm, your headache is gone.

What you've just done is change your body chemistry using the healing power of the mind. By imagining the warmth caressing your hands, you redirected the blood flow to those areas and away from your head.

PRAYER

The Oldest Mind Power of All

Prayer even predates the Bible, which is full of examples of its healing power. But prayer means something different for each of us, depending on individual beliefs and religious backgrounds. Many don't believe in prayer and spiritual faith at all.

Dr. Herbert Benson, author of *The Relaxation Response* and *Beyond the Relaxation Response*, both landmark books in the mind-body field, said his research has convinced him that "faith does make a difference in enhancing the power of the mind over health and disease."

Benson added that when he taught patients to concentrate on a word or phrase to help evoke the relaxation response, about 80 percent chose a prayer

> For students of mind power and now even scientific researchers in laboratories around the world, there is no doubt that prayer and faith have awesome powers to calm the mind, heal the body and bring peace to the soul.

PRAYER

or prayer word – and, incredibly, those who used prayer had improvement rates far superior to those who chose some neutral word or phrase.

Charles Fillmore, co-founder of Unity Church, healed himself through the power of prayer and spiritual ideas. He advised others, "Go first to God and then to man as God directs." In other words, first put your trust in the spiritual side of your nature through prayer and then follow that inner guidance in seeking the treatment.

And Dr. Kenneth Pelletier, the Stanford University psychologist who wrote several books, including the international best seller *Mind As Healer, Mind As Slayer*, studied people who had made astonishing recoveries from life-threatening illnesses. He found they shared several characteristics. The two most important were:

1. Profound changes in their lives through meditation, prayer and other spiritual practices.

2. A deep sense of the spiritual side of their human nature. The healing power of prayer is often misunderstood. It is more than just words, supplications, invocations, entreaties, pleas and affirmations, although all these are vitally important components of healing through prayer. But prayer is also faith, hope and, for many, forgiveness.

> For example, Jesus said, "Thy faith has made thee whole," to someone asking to be healed. In other words, it was the person's own faith, the deep belief in a higher spiritual power, that brought about the healing.

One of the most powerful prayers for healing any condition or situation is one of simple faith: 'I let go and let God'.

Dr. Bernie Siegel, who has helped teach countless cancer patients to heal themselves, said, "In the face of uncertainty, there's nothing wrong with hope." Hope, like faith, is a positive affirmation that enhances the will to live.

The spiritual guide for self-discovery known as *A Course in Miracles* teaches that 'Forgiveness is the key to happi-

PRAYER

> **Endless studies prove that the will to live is one of the most powerful weapons available in the battle against cancer and other life-threatening diseases.**

ness'. And the Bible itself tells us that forgiveness and healing go hand in hand. To forgive really means to let go of any anger, resentments and negativity that are blocking you so the positive, natural healing forces can flow through.

In his booklet *Thought Conditioner*, the Rev. Norman Vincent Peale wrote, "Change your thoughts and you can change anything. The world in which you live is not determined by outward circumstances nearly so much as by the thoughts which habitually occupy your mind."

Rev. Peale then described how to use various biblical verses as healing prayers. These include:

- "What things soever ye desire, when ye pray, believe that ye receive them, and ye shall have them." (Mark 11:24)

"To pray successfully," wrote Peale, "you must employ affirmation and visualization. Form a picture in your mind, not of lack or denial or frustration or illness, but of prosperity, abundance, attainment, health.

"Always remember you will receive as a result of prayer exactly what you think, not what you say. If you pray for achievement but think defeat, your words are idle because your heart has already accepted defeat. Therefore practice believing that even as you pray you are receiving God's boundless blessings and they will come to you."

- "Confess your faults one to another, and pray one for another, that ye may be healed. The effectual fervent prayer of a righteous man availeth much." (James 5:16)

PRAY AND THINK POSITIVE!

"God does heal," Peale said. "He does it...through science and through faith. In healing, confession is important, for much illness results from buried resentments and guilt. Confession to a competent counselor releases these poisons, cleanses the mind and soul, thus stopping the passing on of diseased

PRAYER

thoughts to the body. Effectual prayer, that is, scientific prayer, is very powerful. The essence of the technique is confess your faults, pray with kindred spirits even if separated by distance, and enthusiastically (fervently) believe."

● "Ask, and it shall be given you; seek, and ye shall find; knock, and it shall be opened unto you." (Matthew 7:7)

"This is a very practical technique of prayer. It works amazingly. One reason we do not get answers to our prayers is that we ask but do not really expect to receive. We are expert askers, but inexpert receivers. This spiritual formula tells us to ask and then immediately conceive of ourselves as receiving. For example, to be free from fear (or illness), ask the Lord to free you. Then believe that He has immediately done so. The minute you express your faith by sincerely asking Him for a blessing and believe your prayer is answered, your prayer is answered."

● "Whosoever shall say to this mountain, be thou removed, and be thou cast into the sea; and shall not doubt in his heart, but shall believe that those things which he saith shall come to pass, he shall have whosoever he saith." (Mark 11:23)

"Almost alone this passage can revolutionize your life and change defeat into victory (or illness into health). What does it tell you? That your 'mountain', that great rock-like obstruction, that tremendous barrier, can be broken down and ousted from your life. You must not doubt 'in your heart'. Allow no negative thoughts to exist in your subconscious mind. Pray that your mountainous difficulty shall be removed and as you pray believe that it is being done then and now. Don't have the hazy idea that 'this moun-

> Even if you don't consider yourself a 'religious' person, don't reject prayer out of hand or be afraid of it. If it makes it easier, think of it as therapy and the prayer itself as nothing more than a conversation with a Higher Power, Universal Intelligence, Holy Spirit, or any other concept of God that makes you feel comfortable.

tain' may be removed sometime in the future, but believe that God is removing it for you now."

"Prayer is a heart-to-heart verbal or mental conversation with God, as we personally feel God to be for us," said Roy Eugene Davis in his *Easy Guide to Meditation*.

WE HAVE THE POWER

The power to heal lies in everyone's subconscious mind and prayer is one way to create the right mental conditions to release that power. When you pray for a healing, you create in your mind the image you want of yourself as a healthy, disease-free person. By remaining faithful to that image, your prayer is answered – just as spiritual teachers have told us for centuries, regardless of what formal, organized religion they belonged to.

Once you come to believe that your difficulty may be caused by your own negative, unforgiving thoughts that are lodged in your subconscious, you can begin cleaning out the negativity and correcting the erroneous images through prayer.

Never let yourself admit for a second that you might not be healed, and always end by thanking God (or however you define the spiritual force in your life) for the healing that you know is already at work.

Think of yourself as an engineer and your prayers as the tools you use to build a brand new building or, in the case of healing, a brand new you.

Sheri Perl suffered from both ileitis, a disease of the small intestine, and chronic hepatitis. Many times she nearly died before turning to prayer and other mental techniques to heal herself. Based on her own extraordinary experiences, Perl developed a 'Five Phase Healing Program' that includes prayer that she has been teaching to others since 1978. She described the program and her work with seriously or terminally ill patients in *Healing from the Inside Out*.

"Healing from the inside out means going inside to the spiritual source of your power, healing first from the psychic, spiritual, feeling-thought plane and then experiencing the change as the energy filters out into the physical layers of your body," Perl wrote.

"This does not exclude the use of medicine or any techno-

PRAYER

logical advancement that helps you. However, it does most assuredly include working with the contents of your own mind and opening yourself up to new possibilities. It's easy to take a Tylenol when you have a headache and push all this psychic stuff aside, because most likely the headache is going to go away anyway and you don't have to worry. But heaven help you if you come up with a so-called incurable disease, as I did, and you're unwilling to explore the inner psychic content of your being or your universe."

Some of the affirmations of health that Perl uses herself and recommends to her students take the form of prayers.

"I encourage people to make up their own affirmations, of course," Perl added. "Using prayer or affirmations following meditation is even more powerful, as meditation induces an altered state in which the mind is more open to suggestion... Working with meditation, affirmation and prayer has been the greatest factor in creating change in my life."

The work of Dr. Carl Simonton in treating cancer through the use of meditation and guided imagery is well-known. His second book, *The Healing Journey*, has a lot to say about the power of prayer and its effect in so-called miracle healings.

Sheri Perl begins each day with the following affirmation: "I am filling myself with pure white light so that only love and purposefulness, wisdom and health, healing energy, peace and joy will be here now. I release all my past fears, doubts, negatives, relationships and inner self to the light.
I am a light being. My true nature is light. I radiate light from my light center throughout my being to everyone and everything. I now step into a crystal cathedral of light where my angel guides are and the hierarchy is. They send me love and energy and I am well and strong... Only love and light can come here now and only love and light can stay. I receive this, so be it and so it is. Thank you God for everything."

PRAYER

ONE MAN'S INCREDIBLE STORY

Half of Simonton's book is in the form of letters written by a cured patient to other cancer sufferers explaining how he used prayer and other mind power techniques to heal himself.

That patient, Reid Henson, a highly successful businessman in his early 40s, was diagnosed in 1979 with a rare form of cancer, hairy cell leukemia, and told he had two years to live, and probably less. With Simonton's help, Henson embarked on an intensive crusade to develop the healing powers within himself that medical science couldn't give him. Although Henson did not consider himself a religious person, much of the treatment involved prayer and meditation, which for Henson came to mean 'talking to God and listening'.

During one prayerful meditation in September 1981, two years after his doctors pronounced their 'death sentence', Henson underwent what he now calls "a profound spiritual experience."

According to Henson, this is what happened: "At some point, I entered a new state of consciousness that I can't begin to describe. My miraculous spiritual experience began. I did not see a vision. I heard no voices. Yet words appeared, in a startling way, in my mind:

It did not have to be this way.
This is the path you chose.
The tears you are shedding now
Are the tears I shed for you while
You were on an errant course.
This is not the only relationship
You have misunderstood.
I have heard your prayer for
Health and it will be answered in
Due course.

"Immediately doubt began to creep into my mind... And while these doubts were still in the process of forming, they were stopped cold by these words, which were the same in nature and power as the proceeding ones:

'This is real!'

"Immediately all doubt was gone! I knew it was true... I couldn't figure it out. But I did not need to. It was just true."

WHAT IS A MIRACLE?

At the time, Henson was still seriously ill. His blood count was extremely low and he developed a serious infection that put him in the hospital. His doctor didn't have much faith that Henson would pull out of the crisis since his defenses were already depleted by the cancer. But Henson believed in the healing message he had received in prayer and was convinced he would recover.

That was in October 1981. Early in January 1982, the same doctor telephoned Henson with the results of his most recent blood test.

"He said," Henson recalled, "'I don't know what you have been doing, but I hope you'll tell me. Your blood counts are better than mine!' I will never forget my experience, the message I received on September 23, 1981. It is my most treasured memory. I don't need doctors, psychologists, preachers, friends, strangers or anyone else to explain it to me. I know what happened!"

Dr. Simonton was delighted with Reid Henson's astonishing recovery and the apparent miracle healing he experienced. But he wasn't surprised. Simonton had seen it happen before with other cancer patients who were 'supposed' to die.

"A miracle," Dr. Simonton observed, "is an event or action that apparently contradicts known scientific laws and is hence thought to be due to supernatural causes, especially to an act of God. You can decide for yourself whether or not Reid's healing fits that definition.

"I believe that Reid had a direct communication from God. At the same time, I believe that everything is part of God. If the message could somehow be proven to have come from Reid's subconscious, that wouldn't make any difference to me. If everything is part of God, then the subconscious is part of God. I myself have had two similar experiences. I know many others who have had them, and I have read of hundreds more.

"Reid had an experience in which he became open to the mystery of life, in which he had a sense of knowing, an intense calm, a feeling that everything was going to be OK. On the deepest level of his being, the fear that had engulfed him was gone. In his heart and in his mind, he knew that he would be well. With that knowing came the appropriate physiological changes in his body."

> **Another misconception about prayers for healing is that they have to follow a prescribed pattern or they won't work. Not so. Prayer can take any form – or no form at all in its truest sense. Prayer can be the formal invocations we learned by rote as children. Prayer can be a chatty, informal conversation with God or that nameless, spiritual force that many think of as universal love. Or it can be a matter of just clearing your mind so that the 'still, small voice' in all of us can be heard above the constant mind chatter.**

While Reid Henson experienced a startling and profound healing through prayer and meditation, Dr. Simonton cautioned that all experiences don't have to be that intense to still be valid healings.

"Honor your feeling," Dr. Simonton says. "Make decisions around it. Make a definite plan and a definite commitment to implement the information. This will help you later if more doubts occur, as they often do especially if you need to make changes in your life that trouble or inconvenience others. Taking action is very important.

"I believe that communication with the universe is possible and learnable... Ask for understanding. Ask for experiences like Reid's. Don't insist on a similar outcome, but have positive expectations about what may be the outcome for you in your unique situation, in your unique way."

It Works Best When You Let Go

It helps to think of prayer and faith as opposite sides of the same coin. In the Bible, Jesus said, "Thy faith has made thee whole." Today, that same faith – a deep belief that a higher spiritual power is at work in our lives – is as powerful as it was in biblical times. The simple act of surrendering or letting go and saying, "Thy will be done," seems to lift an enormous burden and allows the natural, self-healing capacity we possess to take over.

And that power of faith has been demonstrated over and over in the kind of 'miracles' that most mind-body teachers have come to accept as routine but that many doctors still label as 'spontaneous regressions' because they have no other explanation for the healing that takes place.

For example, Jon Kabat-Zinn, the director of the Stress Reduction and Relaxation Program at the University of Massachusetts Medical Center, uses the idea of acceptance that is inherent in faith and prayer with his patients.

"What frequently happens to people in chronic pain," he says, "is that they get so focused on their pain as being 'bad' that their entire lives begin to revolve around it.

"During prayer and healing meditations, they are able to see that pain is just another bodily sensation. They don't have to judge it as either good or bad, so often the chronic pain decreases. In others, the pain is still there but it interferes less in their daily life and with their ability to function."

HEALED BY FAITH ALONE

In *The Healer Within*, Dr. Carl Simonton reported on some startling cases of people who were apparently healed through faith alone. One doctor, he wrote, was treating an especially difficult case of asthma. The doctor obtained a sample of a powerful new medicine that he gave to the patient. To the amazement of both doctor and patient, the improvement was spectacular.

But since the drug was new, the doctor decided to try an experiment. He started giving the patient a harmless placebo in place of the new medication and immediately the patient began to have trouble breathing again.

Convinced that the new drug was effective, he asked the pharmaceutical company for more samples, only to be told that the first sample had, in fact, been a placebo itself that had been sent to him by accident. It was the patient's own faith that he was receiving a miracle drug that had helped his asthma.

In another case, a German doctor was treating three bedridden women. One was dying of cancer of the uterus, another had an inflamed gallbladder and the third was recovering from abdominal surgery for an inflamed pancreas.

Since nothing else had worked, the doctor decided to try faith healing. A local healer was asked to project his healing powers from a distance – each time without success.

Then the doctor told the patients about the healer and how his healing technique had helped other patients. On a certain day, the doctor informed the three women, the healer would beam his powers at them.

Incredibly, the woman with the pancreas problem began to recover and gained 30 pounds. The patient with the gallstones went home totally recovered. The cancer patient's disease had advanced so far nothing could be done. But the quality of her life improved so much that she was able to return home and live three more months almost pain-free.

The three were not told that on the day of the supposed healing, the faith healer had, in fact, done nothing.

"Faith made these women physically stronger, in one instance strong enough to recover completely," Simonton reported. **"Faith in the unseen, unfelt medical force was responsible for the dramatic transformation, but it would be a mistake to assume that only the belief in medical or quasi-medical rituals can work such marvels."**

Messages from the Subconscious

Dreams have been with us forever. Shamans, witch doctors, medicine men and psychiatrists – from ancient days to modern times – have been interpreters of these mysterious messages from the subconscious. Freud called dreams "the royal road to the unconscious," and since then, countless books have been written attempting to explain the fantastic, bizarre symbols that make up our dream lives.

However, dreams and the specific healing messages they convey – like so many mysteries that fall under the broad umbrella of 'psychic phenomena' – have too often been ignored and rejected.

Here's what Dr. Carl Simon-

> **Specialists in mind-body research look seriously at dreams and their contents as rich sources of information about the things that make us sick – and how to make us better. What they've discovered is providing us with some startling new healing techniques.**

ton had to say about that problem in his landmark book *Getting Well Again*:

"The means by which the unconscious communicates with the conscious self is through feelings, dreams and intuition. Unfortunately, our culture seems to undervalue these messages. We tend to ignore the feelings, dreams and intuition from our internal self which are attempting to provide us with resources to meet the demands of the external world.

"It has been hypothesized by several researchers that cancer patients may have been cut off from the resources of their unconscious processes. In our experience, many recovered patients have come to see their illness as, in part, a message to value and pay more attention to their unconscious self rather than to the demands of others. In addition, many patients have described having had specific insights, feelings, dreams or images which provided valuable guidance in their efforts to regain their health."

Dr. Bernie Siegel considers dreams so important to the healing process that he puts them at the top of his list of things to do to heal your life and cure your afflictions:

DREAMING YOURSELF WELL

"Keep a daily journal recording your feelings and dreams. In tests of college students and executives, those individuals who had been asked to keep journals were shown to have a more active immune system and to develop fewer colds and other illnesses during exam time and periods of work stress. Even after they stopped keeping the journals, the immune system remained more active for up to six months. Including periodic drawings may also help."

Like other mind-body teachers who have learned how vital it is to trust our dreams, Dr. Siegel urges anyone searching for a clearer insight into their own health and emotional fitness to keep a journal at their bedside to keep a record of their dreams.

Keeping a record of dreams means they'll surface consciously more often and with a clearer connection to the ailment afflicting you.

DREAMS

Since most of the mind-body healing takes place on an unconscious level, one of the best ways to understand what is happening on that level, and therefore diagnose physical illnesses, is to study the messages from the unconscious that appear in dreams.

Dr. Siegel told of one patient who already had breast cancer, but who dreamed her head was shaved and the word *cancer* was written on her scalp. The message: The cancer had spread to her brain, although there were no symptoms or physical signs. Three weeks later, tests confirmed the dream was true.

THE 'DIRECT INSIGHT' DREAM

"I once had a dream during a time when I was having certain symptoms that might have been due to cancer," Dr. Siegel continued. "In my dream I was a member of a group whose other members all had cancer, but I was pointed out as not having it. Tests later verified what the dream had communicated.

"One day in the operating room I was discussing dreams and a nurse recounted one of her 'direct insight' dreams. She had been very sick for several weeks, and no one could figure out what was wrong. Then one night she had a dream in which a shellfish opened, a worm stood up inside it, and an old woman pointed at the worm and said, 'That's what's wrong with you'. The nurse woke up knowing she had hepatitis, which was confirmed by subsequent tests."

Sheri Perl, who described her own extensive self-healing in *Healing from the Inside Out*, also used a dream notebook to record dreams and later sort out the healing messages they were communicating to her.

"If you are not doing it already, pay closer attention to your dreams," Perl advises. "Recurring themes can tell you a good deal about your beliefs and state of mind."

Here's one example of how a dream directly affected a healing when the dreamer asked the right questions. In her book *Living in the Light*, mind-body teacher Shakti Gawain reported, "One of my friends had been having severe pain on the right side of her face. Intuitively, she

> Don't be discouraged if answers don't emerge in your dreams the first few times you try. Be persistent and they'll come. After awhile, you might even find that your dreams are telling you what to focus on in your waking life. However, the answers that appear may need some interpretation and since your dreams come from your inner self, you yourself are the best interpreter. When you try to interpret your dreams, ask yourself what associations you make with the images depicted in your dreams. How did the dream make you feel? And how do those images and feelings relate to your daily life and to the kind of healing you're seeking?

felt the pain would ease if she'd open her mouth and state more of what she wanted and more of what she knew. She did this and the pain eased some, but it still wasn't gone. One night, in a mood of surrender, she told the universe she was sick of the whole thing, and she asked for an answer.

"Then she let go of thinking about the problem and went to sleep. In her dreams that night her intuition told her to stop taking brewer's yeast. She immediately discounted the entire message as bizarre and continued to take yeast. But a few days later, after continued prodding from her insides, she stopped taking yeast. Two days later, her face pain cleared up."

Dr. Brian Weiss, who broke new ground in past-life recall therapy with his landmark best sellers, *Many Lives, Many Masters* and *Through Time into Healing,* says that dreams, along with hypnosis, are powerful tools for opening the doorway to past lives and energizing the healing process.

Give your dream a label or title that identifies its general theme or content. This also helps you retrieve it later for more elaboration. Write as many of the dreams as you can recall in the journal you keep at your bedside.

Like others in the field, Dr. Weiss says that keeping a dream journal is essential if you

DREAMS

hope to uncover the key to healing that may lie hidden in past lives. Not all dreams, he says, are the type that Freud studied – that is, full of symbols, wishes and distortions. Dreams can also contain valuable clues to past lives. Others may actually be literal memories of a past life or lives.

DREAMS CAN REVEAL PAST LIVES

In using a dream journal to aid in past-lives recall, Dr. Weiss suggests that as soon as you awaken, remain quiet and try not to move. Remember as much of your dream or dreams as possible. As you fix it firmly in your mind, additional details may emerge.

"The more dreams you record, the more clues about your past lives you may receive," writes Dr. Weiss. "You can recognize a dream that holds a clue from a past life when you find you have dreamed you were dressed in clothing from a different period of time or when you are using tools or other implements that seem to date from a different place or time... You don't need to determine immediately the meaning of the clue. Simply write a narrative, give the dream a name, and occasionally review the contents of your entire journal for trends or patterns.

"Do the details seem interrelated or random? Details of other places and times that can be integrated into a theme or picture may be giving you indications of the most important or relevant past lives for exploration, while the more random ones may be just that, random details, or else memory fragments that are not yet organized."

Later, when you want to explore in more detail a past life that has emerged from your dreams, go into meditation and focus your mind on the theme that you recorded in your dream journal.

Visualize the scene as it was in your dream, even if it's only a fragment. In the quiet of your meditation, allow that image to expand and continue, much like restarting a movie film that was halted, and try not to inhibit, influence or censor the impression of the other life that flows through your consciousness.

DREAMS

"A fairly complete past-life memory might evolve from a single meditation, or over several, or not at all," Dr. Weiss states.

"In the beginning it is common to receive a collection of past-life fragments that do not seem coherent. The more you practice this technique, the more skilled you will become."

Unbelievable as it sounds, it's possible to 'wake up' inside your dreams, consciously participate in them, and assume control over those fantastic events.

You've probably had spontaneous 'lucid' dreams without knowing what they were called. Almost everyone has experienced the eerie sensation of becoming aware that you're dreaming while knowing your body is still asleep. What's even more amazing, and what very few people realize, is that they also have the power to shape the outcome of the dream.

Lucid dreams can play a vital role in healing for this reason: In lucid dreaming, you have the ultimate and absolute power to change the dream and shape it in any way you choose, and mind-body researchers tell us that when you change your dreams, you're also changing your conscious reality. The evidence is clear that the benefits gained and the lessons learned during lucid dreaming can affect everyday life.

"It goes both ways," says Dr. Jane Garfield, a dream expert who conducts classes on lucid dreaming. "What you're thinking about in the waking state affects dreams. Experiences in your dream state carry over into waking life."

If you encounter an obstacle in a lucid dream, or confront some frightening person or thing, you know that, since you are dreaming, the person or object only represents something in you.

Does it symbolize a disease? A symptom of a developing disease? What steps can you take in your waking life to prevent or cure it?

For example, a student in one of Dr. Garfield's lucid dreaming classes was a drum maker who often injured his hands while working. But he discovered that he could speed the healing during lucid dreaming in which he watches his hands heal before his very eyes. After such a dream, his hands heal much more rapidly in his waking life.

DREAMS

LUCID DREAMS HELP HEALING

In other words, many people who are already good at healing through creative visualization find they heal even faster with lucid dreaming because the process seems more real to them.

"When you have a lucid dream, the nervous system is registering it very close to reality," Dr. Garfield explains. Dr. Stephen LaBerge of Stanford University, one of the top experts on lucid dreaming, says that about one out of every 10 people is a natural lucid dreamer. And those who don't come by this marvelous skill naturally can still pick it up with a little practice and determination.

If you're receptive to the idea and sincerely want to experience lucid dreams, you've already taken the first major step. The next step is to start giving yourself suggestions that you will have a lucid dream every night before you fall asleep.

Tell yourself that you're going to remember even ordinary dreams – and when you do, record them in a dream journal or keep a tape-recorder beside your bed so you can dictate your dreams before they fade.

Study those dream memories for details about what they might be trying to tell you. For instance, if a certain image, person, scene or event keeps popping up, train yourself to ask each time it appears whether or not you're dreaming. This lets you get a foot in the door of the unconscious. With practice, and once your dreams know you're outside knocking to get in, the next level takes you inside the dream and suddenly you're lucid dreaming with full control over what happens.

How to 'Wake up' inside Your Dreams

Do some deep relaxation practice and totally clear your mind. Hold your hands in front of you at arm's length and repeat to yourself, "I see my hands in my dream; I know I am dreaming." Then refocus on a blank wall or some other neutral object that your dream journal tells you often appears in your dreams and repeat the process several times a day.

Another method is to hold

on to consciousness as you're falling asleep. Observe the images passing through your mind and focus on that feeling, which is similar to the sensation of lucid dreaming. And when you wake in the morning, while your mind is still half asleep, try to 'redream' the dreams you had.

> **You can immediately tell the difference between ordinary and lucid dreams. First of all, you know you're dreaming. Lucid dreams are more realistic and fewer people or characters will be involved.**

To really have an impact on the outcome of your dream, try to maintain a detached feeling about what is happening. And try to stay aware of the fact that you are lucid dreaming so you don't revert to regular dreaming.

And, most important of all, you know you are in control and have all the magnificent powers of the mind at your disposal to work on your healing. However, even if you don't perfect the lucid dreaming technique, Dr. Garfield says you can still have enormous influence over your dreams and their power to heal through methods she outlined in her books *Creative Dreaming* and *Healing Power of Dreams*.

The basic concept of creative dreaming, like lucid dreaming, is to become more of being an active participant in the action. By fighting back or confronting the trouble (which may appear in your dreams as a monster), you take active steps to start the healing process.

"I believe," Dr. Garfield has said, "that by practicing within a dream – by changing the dream – you not only deal with the difficult situation in the dream, but you also carry over to the waking state an attitude that allows you to cope more effectively. The more aware you become in your dream state while you're in it, the more you can use dreams to your benefit."

The dream journal is also a critical element in creative dreaming. With a collection of dreams, you're better able to detect a pattern in what your dreams are conveying to you. Also, later dreams often add important meaning to earlier ones.

Whatever the goal you have

DREAMS

in mind, whether it's a physical healing or something else, Dr. Garfield recommends concentrating fully on that desire during your waking state. Throughout the day, fill your mind with what you want to experience or accomplish in your dreams.

To enhance your concentration, be sure to use a short, simple phrase that describes your goal – "Tonight I will be healed," for example. Repeat the affirmation as you fall asleep, when the mind is most susceptible to suggestions.

Some deep breathing, progressive relaxation, visualization and meditation techniques also prepare the subconscious mind for the healing dream work to follow. Look at the appropriate sections in this book for details on these techniques.

> **In the morning, when you awaken naturally, without the jangle of an alarm clock, lie still with your eyes closed. In the serenity of the moment, let the memory of your dreams flow through your mind. Try to recapture the images, even if they're only fragments or vague feelings. As the scene unfolds, more details will emerge.**

INNER GUIDES

A Warm and Loving Friend

Newcomers to mind-body healing often find, to their absolute amazement, that someone or something – some tender, loving presence – is waiting to help and guide them when they enter that unexplored territory of the subconscious.

Mind-body teachers aren't surprised when these inner guides or advisers appear. In fact, many methods encourage patients to consciously search for that inner guidance.

Whatever this mysterious presence is, its main purpose is to gently guide you in terms

> Spiritualists and mystics have known about inner guides for centuries. Some call it the 'still, small voice' that directs us to our higher good and fulfills our needs. Other mystics say it is 'the spirit of life that is always speaking to our souls'. For the less spiritually inclined, it's simply called intuition, but intuition developed to a high degree of awareness.

INNER GUIDES

of physical healing that can take many forms.

Psychologists Bernie Zilbergeld and Arnold Lazarus talked about the value of inner guides in *Mind Power: Getting What You Want through Mental Training:*

"Many of us believe that there is some part of us that is wiser and more mature than the rest of the parts of our being. This part is variously called the strong part, the healthy part, the guide or the inner adviser. Whatever the name, it's often believed that we'd be a lot better off if we paid more attention to this part and took its advice.

"This part is only an aspect of you, consisting of memories, experiences and resources that may not be readily available to your everyday self. The inner-adviser technique is a way of getting in touch with this part and being able to discern its messages.

"If you want to contact your inner adviser, you have to be open to surprises. Our guides aren't always what we expect. Its gender may not be the same as yours, it may be an animal rather than a person, it may communicate in ways you're not used to and it may be a tough taskmaster instead of friendly and supportive as you expected. But that isn't surprising. Surely you've had the experience of an inner voice suggesting that you do something...that the rest of you didn't agree with."

LEARN TO TRUST THAT VOICE

This is especially true when it comes to healing. Even though we understand that the answers we seek lie within us, we're often reluctant to trust ourselves or that still, small voice – even though we might obey without question if the guidance came from a medical doctor or a psychic faith healer.

We really haven't learned to trust our intuition, our inner self, when it's trying to tell us something. Therefore, many mind-body teachers encourage patients to visualize a wise, all-knowing guide or guru who will never fail to provide the right answers that they can trust. Many other seekers, however, meet up with their guides unexpectedly and spontaneously as they journey by themselves ever deeper into the kingdom of the mind.

INNER GUIDES

Most inner guides they meet appear as respected figures – wise men or women, doctors, teachers or religious figures.

But not always. Dr. David Bresler teaches patients at the UCLA Medical School Pain Clinic to use the inner guides as a source of information about their pain. He often suggests that the guides appear as lighthearted fantasy figures or humorous animals.

Regardless of their form, inner guides come equipped with answers to questions about healing that are otherwise beyond the patient's ability to know on a conscious level.

If you're apprehensive about making that journey yourself, and uneasy about who or what you might run into along the way, then take heart from the following stories about inner guides reported by the world's leading mind-body experts.

In *Relaxation and Imagery*, Rothlyn Zahourek tells the story of Beth, a young nurse recovering from breast cancer following surgery. But the healing process was slow and Beth complained of severe, constant pain in her back "...like a tiger clawing at me." Pain medication didn't help. When Beth tried the inner adviser technique, she met a tiger who told her he had been trying to get her attention by clawing at her. From the tiger, Beth discovered that she had become a nurse just to please her parents and the resentment she felt produced the cancer. The tiger told Beth the pain would become bearable once she decided what she wanted to do. After several sessions, the pain did ease considerably.

A teacher named Warren worked every evening on his new house. When he began experiencing strange, unexplainable injuries – pulled back muscle, sprained thumb, broken toe – Warren's wife urged him to try contacting an inner guide to discover why he was constantly hurting himself. After scoffing at the suggestion, Warren finally agreed.

He learned to meditate and discovered a guide in the form of a Native American woman who told him he was being pulled in so many directions that he was injuring himself. Following the guide's advice to cut his time working on the house in half, Warren incurred no additional injuries.

INNER GUIDES

Dr. Carl Simonton describes numerous cases of his patients benefiting tremendously from their contact with the inner guides. In fact, Simonton calls the guides "...an important mental resource from which you are usually cut off."

INNER GUIDE DOCTOR

One of the patients Simonton discussed in *Getting Well Again* was John, 18, who had acute leukemia. One night he dreamed about an 'unorthodox doctor' who claimed to be a healer with the power to help John defeat the disease.

Later, John had reestablished contact with the 'doctor' during a mental imagery session and talked to him about his loss of weight and lack of physical exercise. The 'doctor's' advice included asking the hospital dietitian for a special 1,500-calorie protein drink every day. John quickly began putting on weight and felt better than he had in months.

Dr. Simonton described Gwen, another cancer patient, as difficult to work with. She often resisted self-examination or refused to look at new ways of relating to people. Simonton suggested she try contacting an inner guide during a mental imagery process and was surprised when Gwen told him that a figure she had named 'Dr. Fritz' had appeared spontaneously in her mental imagery two months earlier.

When she asked Dr. Fritz what he was doing in her mind, he told her he was there to help her get well. As Gwen continued to question Dr. Fritz, she discovered he knew everything about the emotional problems she had been avoiding.

Gwen reported 30 or 40 such 'consultations' with Dr. Fritz over the next six months – and her health steadily improved.

> **Following an angry telephone call with her daughter, Gwen's cancer pain flared up. When she consulted with Dr. Fritz about the pain, he told her it was because she hadn't resolved the conflict with her daughter. As soon as Gwen called her daughter back and settled the problem, the pain began to fade.**

INNER GUIDES

Even Dr. Bernie Siegel, who has taught thousands to cope with and even heal their cancer, learned about inner guides from Dr. Simonton. In his own book, *Love, Medicine & Miracles*, Dr. Siegel described the amazing, close encounter with his rather peculiar inner guide during a session of directed meditation.

"I approached this exercise with all the skepticism one expects from a mechanistic doctor," he wrote. "I didn't believe it would work, but if it did I expected to see Jesus or Moses.

"Instead I met George, a bearded, long-haired young man wearing an immaculate flowing white gown and a skullcap. It was an incredible awakening for me... George was spontaneous, aware of my feelings and an excellent adviser. He gave me honest answers, some of which I didn't like at first.

"I was still toying with the idea of a career change. When I told him, he explained that I was too proud to give up the hard-won technical proficiency of surgery and start from scratch in another discipline. Instead, he told me I could do more good by remaining a surgeon but changing myself to help my patients mobilize their mental powers against disease. I could combine the support and guidance of a minister or psychiatrist with the resources and expertise of a physician.

"I could practice 'clergery', a term my wife coined. In the hospital I could be a role model for students, house officers and even other physicians.

"George said, 'You can go anywhere in the hospital. A clergyman or therapist can't. You are free to supplement medical treatment with love or death-and-dying counseling, in a way that nonphysicians are not.' George...has been my invaluable companion ever since his first appearance. My life is much easier now, because he does the hard work."

Get in Touch with Your Guide

There are many different methods of contacting your own inner guide and benefiting from the immense storehouse of knowledge about yourself and your healing process that the guide can provide. A few of the more successful, easy-to-follow methods are included here. Find the one that feels most comfortable for you.

Dr. Simonton's 'inner guide

INNER GUIDES

mental imagery process' is one he describes as "uniformly valuable in aiding our patients' recoveries." He encourages others to use the following process to make the initial contact with an inner guide:

1. Sit in a comfortable chair, feet flat on the floor, eyes closed. Use the relaxation process to get very comfortable and relaxed.

2. In your mind's eye, see yourself in a natural setting that gives you a feeling of warmth, comfort, peace and serenity. Try to experience the place with all your senses – as if you were really there.

3. Notice a path emerging near you and reaching toward the horizon. Picture yourself walking along this path. It is pleasant and light.

4. In the distance there is a radiant glow that is moving slowly toward you. There is nothing threatening or fearful about the experience.

5. As the glow comes closer, you realize it is a living creature – a person you don't know, or maybe a friendly animal.

6. As the person or creature comes closer, become aware of the details of its appearance. Is the creature masculine or feminine? See its shape and form as clearly as you can. If your guide is a person, notice details of face, hair, eyes, bone structure, build.

7. If this person or creature makes you feel warm, comfortable and safe, you know it is an inner guide.

8. Ask the guide's name, and then ask for help with your problems.

9. Engage the person or creature in a conversation, get acquainted and discuss your problems as you would with a very close friend.

10. Pay careful attention to any information you receive from your guide. It may come in the form of conversation or through symbolic gestures, such as the guide's pointing toward something or producing an object that represents its advice.

11. Establish an agreement with your guide about how to make contact for future discussions.

12. Then when you are ready, let your consciousness come back slowly into the room

INNER GUIDES

where you are sitting and open your eyes.

Psychotherapist Robbie Gass developed a four-step program for use in the workshops he conducts on mind-body connections.

Gass begins with what he calls 'centering'. Before you can reach the source of your inner guide or wisdom you have to become quiet and center yourself in this quiet zone. Any process of quieting your mind and relaxing will work for this first step.

MAKE CLEAR WHAT YOU WANT

Once this is achieved, move to the next step of 'asking'. Make your questions simple and direct. The more precise you are about what it is you want to know, the more likely you are to get a clear answer. After you've asked your questions, you're ready for the 'receiving' step. This is a time to listen calmly for your guide to answer. The receiving stage involves more than just listening. The answers you seek may come in many different forms – spoken words you actually hear or printed words you read, as symbols or graphic pictures or perhaps as body sensations or emotional feelings.

"The information you are asking for already exists," Gass has reported. "When the answer seems to come instantaneously, as if it just pops out, this is usually a good indication that it is accurate information."

Last of all, there's the 'application'. With all your questions about your health and healing now answered, it's up to you to figure out how to apply that information in your daily life.

Rothlyn Zahourek says that the concept of inner guides or inner dialogue is based on the idea that there is a part of all of us that instinctively knows what to do to make us healthier and happier.

Her suggestions for contacting and consulting with your personal inner adviser include: Choose a time when you're not rushed. Use some relax-

> **If we can get in touch with that self-healing source, all the answers we'll ever need are there waiting for us.**

INNER GUIDES

ation techniques to completely relax your body and quiet your mind.

Go to the meditation place where you are comfortable and at peace. Focus on the image of your inner guide, and wait peacefully and expectantly for the guide to appear. Get a clear picture of what the guide looks like – size, shape, sex, age, dress – so that the guide assumes a personality you can identify.

Get Comfortable with Your Guide

Find a comfortable physical distance between you and the guide and start getting acquainted. Find out something about who your adviser is. Then ask the questions about your health problems that are troubling you.

When you feel your questions have been answered, or you're satisfied with the encounter, thank your guide, say goodbye and slowly return to conscious awareness.

But that shouldn't be the end of the experience. Give yourself a pat on the back for making progress. Finally, have a specific plan in mind on how to put into actual practice the information your guide has provided.

Don't worry if these early conversations with your guide seems strange at first and maybe even a little silly. On the other hand, they may feel perfectly natural and normal. Take whatever comes without judging it.

PAST LIVES

Clues that Can Make You Well

Past-life recall, or regression therapy, as it's also called, is one of the latest – and certainly the most astonishing – of all the healing powers of the mind.

The leading authority on past-life therapy is Dr. Brian Weiss, the Miami, FL, psychiatrist who unintentionally stumbled onto the procedure while treating a patient for depression, phobias and panic attacks. While in a hypnotic trance, the woman suddenly began recounting scenes from a previous lifetime. Weiss, who knew nothing about past-life regression at the time, became convinced of the reality of the experience when the woman also began telling him things about himself and his family she had no way of knowing.

> For those who have undertaken this incredible 'mind journey' into other times and other lives to uncover the root causes of present day illnesses and ailments, it's nothing short of miraculous.

PAST LIVES

The results of Weiss' investigation into the past-lives phenomenon formed the basis for his book *Many Lives, Many Masters*, which has sold millions of copies since it was published in 1988.

Dr. Weiss' second book, *Through Time into Healing* (1992), continues that exploration into the mysterious, uncharted depths of time and the extraordinary power of past-life recall to heal the body, make whole the mind, and comfort the spirit.

"In my experience I have found that past-life regression under hypnosis can be an important part of the treatment...and even the cure of certain chronic symptoms and illnesses," Dr. Weiss says.

"Past-life therapy is particularly effective in treating musculoskeletal pain, headaches that do not respond to medication, allergies, asthma and stress-induced or immune-system-related conditions such as ulcers and arthritis. In some cases, it appears to improve cancerous lesions or tumors. Many patients of mine have been able to stop taking pain medication for formerly debilitating conditions after they experience past-life therapy."

Dr. Weiss' work – and his courage to publicize his new technique – has encouraged other therapists around the world to use past-life recall on their own patients. Their results are just as incredible, and they are enthusiastically reporting accounts of other miraculous healings on the part of patients who have journeyed into the past to confront – and cure – their illness or pain at its original source.

REACH BACK IN TIME AND BE HEALED

"As a therapist or a patient, you don't have to believe in past lives or reincarnation for past-life therapy to work," says Dr. Weiss. "The proof is in the pudding. As more than one fellow psychotherapist has said to me, 'I still don't know if I believe in this past-life stuff, but I use it, and it sure does work!'"

Dr. Weiss and other therapists are now using past-life recall to treat people from all walks of life – business executives, housewives, attorneys, blue-collar workers, even other doctors and religious leaders.

"Regression therapy," Dr. Weiss explains in *Through Time into Healing*, "is the mental act of going back to an earlier time, whenever that time may be, in order to retrieve memories that may still be negatively influencing a patient's present life and that are probably the source of the patient's symptoms...

"The experience of past-life recall often feels the same. It feels as if you are remembering, guiding and healing yourself in a way you do not have to explain or prove. It simply happens; it flows.

"When you feel better as a result of your recall experience, whether a physical symptom has been alleviated, an emotional issue soothed, or you simply feel more confident and peaceful about your life and its direction...you don't need to question the logical validity of the experience you have had. You know it has empowered you to improve the quality of your own life or to receive insight about yourself and others in a very tangible way."

Here are a few as reported by Dr. Weiss: Tricia, a 28-year-old engineer, suffered from temporomandibular joint pain (TMJ), migraines and a stiff neck.

During recall, she remembered a lifetime in Asia Minor about 893 B.C. and another during an even more ancient time when she lived in a cave in what is now Greece. In this lifetime, Tricia described her death in which an enemy warrior stood over her (she was male in that lifetime) and thrust a spear into her face.

The pain she experienced then was similar to the migraine pain she had been suffering in this lifetime. Following the recall, Tricia's migraines eased, while her neck stiffness and TMJ improved enough that she no longer needed pain medication to cope.

Alberto, a radiologist, suffered from severe back pain and spasms for many years. Numerous therapies failed to cure the excruciating pain, and only potent, potentially addictive, painkillers allowed him to deal with the pain and keep on working.

During recall sessions, Alberto discovered that twice in

PAST LIVES

past lives he had died from back injuries.

In one lifetime as a soldier, several centuries in the past, Alberto re-experienced a painful death on a European battlefield and even felt the stabbing pain of the fatal wound. That wound corresponded exactly to the source of his current back pain.

Another patient, Betty, also ended her dependence on medication – and cured herself of asthma and allergies.

During one dramatic regression session, Betty began choking and gasping for air. In the past life she was reliving, Betty was being burned at the stake in the late Middle Ages. The smoke and heat from the fire were searing her lungs. Immediately after the recall ended, Betty's asthma improved remarkably. She stopped using the addictive decongestant. Moreover, the ailments disappeared and the quality of her life improved immeasurably.

Of his experience with Betty, Dr. Weiss had this to say: "I still marvel that such a severe, life-paralyzing, lifelong symptom could resolve literally overnight. It seems miraculous to me. Yet it did, along with most of her other allergies.

"Betty is not the only patient of mine who had healed herself or himself of chronic allergies or respiratory problems through recall of a death experience that included the searing of the lungs or suffocation. Migraine headaches, asthma, respiratory infections and allergies are physical conditions in the current lifetime that seem to have origins in suffering experienced in a previous lifetime. Past physical trauma seems to leave present physical residue."

> **Lacey, a teacher in her 40s, suffered from asthma and a lifelong fear of water. During her first regression under Dr. Weiss' guidance, Lacey saw herself as a child falling from a cliff and drowning. Her most vivid recall was how cold and deep the water was.**

Lacey reentered another lifetime as a young slave in the ancient Near East who worked at making bricks. This time, Lacey suffocated when a wagon of wet straw fell on her. Again, she was able to recall the agony and terror she felt when she couldn't breathe.

Lacey's asthmatic condition improved considerably following the recalls. For the first time in her life, she stopped using her asthma medication.

The healing that occurs during past-life recall may be simply a matter of discovering the past physical origin of a present physical pain. Many patients don't need to undergo complex, long-term therapy to uncover and cure the source of physical pain, discomfort or even some severe illnesses.

Dr. Weiss writes that chronic headaches are one of several conditions of this type that respond quickly to past-life therapy. To demonstrate this point, Dr. Weiss cites the case of his own wife, Carole, who suffered from premenstrual migraine headaches for years.

A neck injury suffered in a car accident made the headaches even worse. Medical specialists had repeatedly told Carole they had no cure for the terrible headaches.

In 1988, Carole sought help through hypnosis. Suddenly,

> **Regardless of their social background, education, economic status or spiritual beliefs, all who experience the realities of living past lives uncover the causes of present day disorders, and, perhaps most important of all, come to understand that they do survive after physical death.**

she saw herself in another life as a peasant living in Central Europe 1,000 years ago.

As the scene opened, Carole, now a male, was running from a mob, angry over her heretical beliefs. She was caught and beaten, with a vicious blow above the left eye, the exact spot where the migraine pain was most severe.

In her present lifetime, the same stabbing pain suddenly struck Carole and spread to her entire head. With the therapist's advice that "you no longer need this pain so let it go," the pain suddenly vanished and the migraine never returned.

PAST LIVES

One more remarkable recovery involved Elaine, a highly regarded psychologist with her own thriving practice. For years, Elaine had suffered from excruciating pains in her neck, shoulders and upper back.

During a hypnotic, past-life regression, Elaine reported seeing nothing but blackness and realized she was blindfolded.

"Then I saw myself from the outside," she continued.

"I was standing on top of a tower, one of those castle towers made of stone. My hands were tied behind my back. I was in my early 20s, and I knew that I was a soldier on the side that had lost the battle.

"Then I felt an excruciating pain in my back... I could feel the lance in my back... Then I felt myself falling, and felt the water of the moat closing around me.

"I've always been terrified of heights and drowning. When I came out of it I was still shaken, and I spent a couple of days in agony. I couldn't even touch my facial bones, the pain was so great. But the next morning when I woke up I thought, 'something's very different.'"

Elaine's back pain and her fear of heights had disappeared.

For Dr. Weiss and other therapists, hypnosis is the most common tool for helping patients explore their past lives in search of healings. But a visit to a therapist's office is not always necessary. Dr. Weiss, for instance, conducts workshops in which he teaches people to conduct their own past-life regression, and, in fact, even recommends that they practice at home.

The workshops and his book contain scripts for relaxation and regression meditation exercises that help people guide their subconscious minds to past lives – and even to the between-life memories that most people report experiencing during the recall sessions.

Writes Dr. Weiss: "Physicists and psychiatrists are becoming the mystics of the '90s. We are confirming what prior mystics intuitively knew: that we are all divine beings. We have known this for thousands of years, but we have forgotten.

"And to know our power and return home, we have to remember what is really true. We have to remember the way."

Past-life recall is one of those ways home.

Laughter is the Best Medicine

Whoever said the words above knew exactly what he or she was talking about.

There is nothing funny about a life-threatening disease, but people are living happy, productive lives today because they learned to laugh when things seemed darkest.

These patients and their supposedly 'miraculous' recoveries are living proof of what mind-body experts have long suspected – that humor is a positive force in life and it's that positive force that helps give us life. Without it, we might just as well give in to our disease and stop fighting, which, unfortunately, is what too many people do.

Norman Cousins was the first to really promote humor as an antidote to cancer and other diseases. Cousins came down with a disease called *ankylosing spondylitis* that destroys the connective tissue holding the spine together.

Doctors diagnosed his ailment as incurable. But Cousins refused to accept that verdict and embarked on his own crusade to find a cure. He discovered that humor and positive

HUMOR

thinking were major factors in getting well. This is what Cousins had to say about his astonishing recovery:

"I have learned never to underestimate the capacity of the human mind and body to regenerate – even when the prospects seem most wretched. The lifeforce may be the least understood force on Earth."

At the time, Cousins was the respected editor of the *Saturday Review*. He documented his recovery in the best seller *Anatomy of an Illness As Perceived by the Patient*. Later, Cousins followed that up with a second best-selling book, *Head First: The Biology of Hope*, in which he reported how others – patients and medical experts – also conquered diseases and infirmities using humor and the positive spirit as powerful allies.

"I had considerable difficulty in moving my limbs and even in turning over in bed," Cousins wrote about his illness. "Nodules appeared on my body, gravel-like substances under the skin, indicating the systemic nature of the disease. At the low point of my illness, my jaws were almost locked."

THE EFFECT OF POSITIVE AND NEGATIVE EMOTIONS

While still in that terrible and painful condition, Cousins said he suddenly remembered reading about the bad effects of negative emotion on body chemistry.

"The inevitable question arose in my mind: What about the positive emotions? If negative emotions produce negative chemical changes in the body, wouldn't the positive emotions produce positive chemical changes?

"Is it possible that love, hope, faith, laughter, confidence and the will to live have therapeutic value?"

Cousins set out to find the answer, and the lessons he learned about humor and positive emotions helped cure him – and have helped countless other people who also faced seemingly hopeless circumstances. With his doctor's cooperation, Cousins began taking massive doses of vitamin C and feeding himself equally

HUMOR

massive doses of positive thinking techniques.

"It was easy enough to hope and love and have faith, but what about laughter?" Cousins continued. "Nothing is less funny than being flat on your back with all the bones in your spine and joints hurting. A good place to begin, I thought, was with amusing movies. Allen Funt, producer of the spoofing television program *Candid Camera*, sent films of some of his classics, along with a motion-picture projector. We were even able to get our hands on some old Marx Brothers films.

"It worked. I made the joyous discovery that 10 minutes of genuine belly laughter had an anesthetic effect and would give me at least two hours of pain-free sleep. When the pain-killing effect of the laughter wore off, we would switch on the motion-picture projector again, and, not infrequently, it would lead to another pain-free sleep interval.

"How scientific was it to believe that laughter – as well as the positive emotions in general – was affecting my body chemistry for the better? We took sedimentation-rate readings just before, as well as several hours after, the laughter episodes. Each time, there was a drop of at least five points. The drop by itself was not substantial, but it held and was cumulative. I was greatly elated by the discovery that there is a physiological basis for the ancient theory that laughter is good medicine."

> **What is significant about laughter is that it creates a mood or setting which invites other positive emotions to move in and go to work. In other words, humor helps make it possible for other good things to happen.**

Within days, Cousins' condition began to improve. Eventually, he was not only pain-free, but back on the tennis court and golf course playing with vigor.

Along with his recovery, Cousins also developed a lifelong fascination with all the healing powers of the mind, not just humor.

He collected stories from other mind-body researchers and patients who had been encouraged to follow his advice

83

HUMOR

on the value of laughter in healing.

"Equally gratifying were the accounts from hospitals of new facilities that featured humor and creativity as integral parts of the hospital program," Cousins wrote.

"The first to respond was St. Joseph's Hospital in Houston, TX. I received a telephone call from Dr. John Stehlin, oncological surgeon and medical researcher, asking if I would come to Houston to participate in the dedication ceremonies of a new feature of the hospital called the Living Room. He said that the cancer floor had been redesigned to accommodate a large room furnished with easy chairs, hi-fi equipment, an art corner, video and audio sets and a library.

" 'You can't imagine a setting more unlike a hospital,' he said. 'You would enjoy seeing how a pleasant environment can brighten the mood of the patients. Amusing films are one of our main props. You will enjoy meeting the nuns. They like the idea of making laughter a regular part of the hospital's philosophy.' "

The Living Room at St. Joseph's was only the first of two dozen or more similar programs at hospitals throughout the country that were created mainly on the basis of Cousins' book.

For example, St. John's hospital in Los Angeles introduced a special, closed-circuit comedy channel so patients can watch comedy films day or night.

Joseph Barbera, creator of Huckleberry Hound and Yogi Bear, presented the children's division of Los Angeles County Hospital with life-size replications of the characters made famous in his TV cartoons to cheer up the wards and give sick kids a chuckle.

Duke University Comprehensive Cancer Center in Durham, NC, instituted what Cousins called "the most far-reaching program of all, in the use of not just humor but also music, art and literature in the treatment of the seriously ill.

"All the aspects of treatment are taken into account – the emotional needs of the patient, the interests or hobbies of the patient that can improve the climate of medical care, inside or outside the hospital, and the use of a 'laugh wagon' that is hardly less in evidence in the corridors of the hospital than the 'pill carts' of the nurses."

The Lively Room at the DeKalb Hospital in Decatur, GA, and a new floor at Shawnee Mission Hospital near Kansas City, also were singled out by Cousins for making humor and creativity important parts of their healing programs.

DON'T GIVE UP ON YOUR DOCTOR

However, Cousins also warned that for all its success in his case, he didn't view laughter as a substitute for traditional medical care. "I also tried to bring the full range of positive emotions into play – love, hope, faith, will to live, festivity, purpose, determination," he wrote.

"Obviously, what worked for me may not work for everyone else... it would be an error and, indeed, irresponsible to suggest that laughter – or the positive emotions in general – have universal or automatic validity. People respond differently to the same things. One man's humor is another man's ho-hum. The treatment of illness has to be carefully tailored to suit the individual patient."

Nevertheless, after Cousins published the account of his astonishing recovery in *Anatomy of an Illness,* several medical investigators and mind-body researchers picked up his ideas about the healing power of humor and positive thinking and began to explore them more fully.

For example, Dr. Kathleen Dillion, a professor of psychology at Western New England College, in Springfield, MA, tested Cousins' claim that laughter enhances healing – and discovered actual, physical proof that it's true. Dr. Dillion analyzed saliva samples taken from people watching humorous videotapes and found that laughter temporarily raised the level of immune-system cells that fight upper-respiratory ailments.

Dr. Raymond A. Moody Jr., the author of *Life after Life*, which examines the near-death experience, also wrote *Laugh after Laugh: The Healing Power of Humor*.

"Over the years I have encountered a surprising number of instances in which, to all appearances, patients have laughed themselves back to health, or at least have used their sense of humor as a very

HUMOR

positive and adaptive response to their illnesses," Dr. Moody wrote.

Moody believes there is a definite link between laughter and longevity – or 'those who laugh best, laugh last'. Because laughter makes you feel better, you're more apt to live longer. He's not alone. Other doctors who specialize in geriatric medicine have concluded that one thing all their healthy, elderly patients have in common is a good sense of humor.

Dr. Moody also wrote about the amazing healing power of clowns.

"I have a very good friend who is an internationally known clown. He has made a rule for himself that as often as he can, after a performance, he'll go by the local children's hospital and just walk through the wards, entertaining people. Otherwise, he says, he feels like it's a waste of makeup.

"One day I was talking with him about my observations about medical uses of humor and how humorous interventions can sometimes help people back to health... He said, 'Sure, I do that all the time', and then described a case involving a little girl of about 12 who was in a kind of catatonic state for a long time.

"He walked in on this little girl to entertain her, and she immediately perked up and started to say his name over and over, whereupon the nurse who had been feeding the child just threw down the spoon and went running off to get the doctors, because this was a miracle. My friend was able to work with this child in such a way that she started talking again, and this effect lasted.

"Another clown friend of mine told me about how he went in

> **Dr. Moody and others tell us that a good belly laugh is a great pain fighter. For example, Dr. Moody says that tension in the muscles causes or increases the intensity of a headache. But when people laugh, the tension in the muscles decreases and the pain subsides. Dr. Moody said that a physician he knows has great success curing his patients' tension headaches just by making them laugh.**

HUMOR

to see a 90-year-old man who was literally dying of depression and starving himself to death. The doctors had tried everything, but nothing worked. This clown friend of mine went in and within about 30 minutes this fellow was laughing and talking and eating again, and he actually went on to live several more years. This intervention brought him back."

Other scientific studies have shown that laughter signals the brain to release endorphins, the body's natural pain-killers. Also, laughter is an excellent anesthesia because it draws attention away from our pain.

HUMOR AS A STRESS FIGHTER

Humor is not only a great healer, it is also a great stress-reliever. In fact, Dr. George Vaillant, a renowned Harvard University researcher, endorsed humor as a major stress-coping mechanism among healthy men. Humor and laughter relieve tension, break up any negative thinking patterns that may be holding us back and helps us put everything into perspective.

Dr. Bernie Siegel is such a firm believer in the power of laughter that he thinks that since every hospital room has a TV set, "I hope someday we have a 'healing channel' that includes plenty of comedy, as well as music, meditation and healing imagery."

As a matter of fact, many hospitals now provide 'laughter rooms' where patients can listen to comedy and enjoy the healing effects of humor.

> "There are three levels of humor," says Dr. Harry Olson. "Sarcasm is one, but that's destructive. The second, a good pun that gives you a twist of expectancy has positive qualities. And so does the third level, cosmic humor, which is an appreciation of the paradoxes and absurdities of life. The person who has this level of humor is more likely to be flexible and able to take in stride what life dishes out."

HUMOR

Allen Funt, who helped Cousins recover, has established a Laughter Therapy Institute that makes *Candid Camera* shows available for laughter therapy in hospitals.

Besides all its other healing benefits, a good laugh is also good exercise. When Norman Cousins called laughing 'internal jogging', he knew.

LAUGHTER AS EXERCISE

Stanford University professor Dr. William Fry Jr. studied how laughter affects the body physically, as well. He discovered that when we laugh heartily muscles become active, the heart rate goes up, and respiration increases – exactly the same benefits we get from physical exercise. "Muscles in the face, arms, legs and stomach get a mini-workout (remember how your stomach ached the last time you laughed really hard?) and so do the diaphragm, the thorax and the circulatory and endocrine systems," Dr. Fry added.

Obviously, people who have been told they have a terminal illness and are in pain don't feel they have much to laugh about. But even if a joke or a situation doesn't seem humorous, at least pretend it is. That's a start, even if you're just going through the motions. When you decide that humor is going to be a part of your therapy, sooner or later, the real laughter will come out.

Ever since Norman Cousins described humor as a major force in his self-healing, much attention and research has been focused on the role of positive emotions for enhancing the healing process.

Cousins himself summed it up best when he said, "Illness is not a laughing matter. Perhaps it ought to be. Laughter moves your internal organs around. It enhances respiration. It is an igniter of great expectation."

Laughter is, indeed, the best medicine. And don't worry. You can't overdose on it!

BIOFEEDBACK AND MORE

More Super Healing Tips

Biofeedback, journal writing and music are not – strictly speaking – healing powers of the mind.

But they are among the best outside tools to help unlock those inside powers that promote healing. Here is how you can use these mind-body aids in your own self-healing program.

Biofeedback has helped millions of people achieve some remarkable results, make some astonishing recoveries and, most important of all, discover how they can tap into the boundless and truly astonishing power of their own minds.

The ultimate goal of biofeedback is to show people that with mind-body techniques like relaxation or meditation, they can take charge of their bodies and even control such disorders as epilepsy, chronic pain and asthma.

Using biofeedback techniques, people have learned how to lower their blood pressure, regulate their body temperature, control the amount of acid secreted in their stomachs, or increase the alpha wave frequency in their brains, among other things.

BIOFEEDBACK AND MORE

Sufferers of migraine headaches, hypertension and an unusual ailment called Raynaud's disease, in which the arteries of the fingers and toes constrict, have found tremendous relief using biofeedback.

Initially, biofeedback patients are hooked up to machines that record what's going on in the body – temperature, muscle tension, skin surface temperature, brain wave activity and pulse. The machines monitor those activities and then act like mirrors to 'show' us what our bodies are doing that we can't otherwise see. The changes we can see recorded on the machines (lower heart rate, less tension) show patients that the mind can affect the body.

People learn to modify body activities by listening to a tone or watching a light that is activated when they consciously try to change some bodily function – slowing their heart rate, for instance, or increasing the blood flow to their hands or feet.

The advantage of biofeedback is that patients can see and hear for themselves and, while it's happening, realize that the mind-body connection really works. For many people, that's all the proof they need to take over mind-body training *without* needing the machines.

> **Biofeedback research has finally made us realize what yogis and other mystics have been trying to tell us for centuries – that our conscious minds do have enormous power to control what are usually called the 'involuntary' actions of our bodies.**

Dr. Bernard Brucker, a psychologist at Jackson Memorial Medical Center in Miami, is taking the idea of biofeedback several steps beyond what even the experts once thought possible.

Using high-tech electronics and computers, Brucker is wiring patients suffering from brain or spinal cord damage up to the EMG and the EEG monitors. The first measures the electrical activity in muscles; the second shows what's happening in the brain.

Thousands of patients have reawakened damaged nerves and muscles using the high-

BIOFEEDBACK AND MORE

tech biofeedback methods – many who had lost the use of their limbs entirely have shown amazing improvement.

Other examples of the importance of biofeedback in forging the mind-body link so healing can take place are equally dramatic.

Dr. George Fuller von Bozzay describes the case of a five-year-old girl who came to the Biofeedback Institute of San Francisco afflicted with severe asthma.

Within minutes of 'playing' with the machine, she learned to raise and lower the skin temperature in her hand.

Next, the youngster learned to use those same skills to aid her breathing. In her mind, she imagined that her chest was a balloon that she was filling with air and then emptying as she breathed.

Before the biofeedback training, the child spent about one week per month in the hospital's intensive care ward being treated for asthma attacks. After learning the mind-body techniques, she went years without suffering a severe attack.

Other children worked with biofeedback machines that measured the muscle tension in their faces. After a short period of training, they learned to relax the fine muscles in their faces – and that relaxation significantly improved their breathing.

Diabetics also have reported amazing improvement after biofeedback training. One woman, who experiences serious hyperglycemia (a high level of sugar in the blood) during periods of stress, took biofeedback training to help her learn relaxation techniques. Within six months, the problem with hyperglycemia attacks practically disappeared. As a bonus, she also cut her insulin need in half.

Biofeedback techniques include visualization which we've discussed earlier.

"An important aspect of biofeedback, called visual imagery, was also a principal component of other techniques we had studied," Dr. Carl Simonton observed in *Getting Well Again*. "The more we learned about the process, the more intrigued we became.

"Essentially, the visual imagery process involved a period of relaxation during which the patient would mentally picture a desired goal or result.

With the cancer patient, this would mean his attempting to visualize the cancer, the treatment destroying it and, most importantly, his body's natural defenses helping him recover."

KEEPING A JOURNAL

Experts can't explain exactly why, but somehow writing about the fear and anxiety you feel over your illness or disorder has an amazing ability to speed the healing process.

In *The Healing Journey*, for example, Dr. Simonton emphasizes the importance of a journal for his cancer patients as a means of recording their deepest thoughts or emotions and for keeping track of their experiences with the disease.

"Write down what you think and how you feel about what you've learned thus far," he advises. "Keep these notes to evaluate your progress as you learn more.

"**Your emotions are a result of your beliefs and thoughts, so if you want to feel better, you need to think healthier. Write down what you learn from looking at your thoughts and emotions in retrospect. Be especially aware of how your thoughts and beliefs create emotions.**

"If you haven't done so before, make a list of things that make you feel better. Ask yourself directly, 'What can I do to improve the way I feel?' Do one of those things today... Do this as an exercise in learning to trust that you can influence the way you feel...

"The ultimate goal is to select which thoughts you want to hold and which ones you want to change. You can achieve this by continuing to examine your beliefs and by changing your beliefs to produce positive or neutral emotions."

Dr. Simonton encourages his patients to use writing along with their meditation practice. He suggests that before they begin meditating they write down in the journal exactly what they think their pain is protecting them from. He also has them describe on paper what their beliefs are about that subject.

Patients are then instructed to write down some healthier beliefs on a separate page and

BIOFEEDBACK AND MORE

keep that list handy so they can open their eyes and look at it from time to time while meditating.

Keeping a diary or journal this way is a powerful means of keeping in close touch with our thoughts and, in the case of a disease such as cancer, for measuring progress. Seeing how far they've come compared to where they've been is a positive reinforcement for most patients. Writing is a way of encouraging themselves to continue the battle and work even harder.

Another mind-body teacher, Shakti Gawain, believes that writing journals and affirmations (positive personal statements) can produce some of the fastest, most dramatic healings "because the written word has so much power over our minds. We are both writing and reading them at the same time, so it's actually like a double hit of energy."

For writing affirmations, Gawain suggests the following technique: Begin with an affirmation, preferably one you make up yourself, that focuses on your own special problem or need – "I am growing stronger every day," or "I am filled with divine healing," are just two examples.

Write that affirmation at least 10 or 20 times in succession. To increase its effectiveness, include your name in the affirmation so that it might read, "I, John, am growing stronger every day," or "You, John, are filled with divine healing."

Just writing the words isn't enough, however. Really concentrate on the words as you write. Watch how you feel about what you're writing. And avoid resistance, negative thoughts, or doubts that the affirmation will really help you.

> **Dr. Bernie Siegel says journal writing is really a type of meditation and carries many of the same benefits. A journal or diary, he adds, "makes us aware how active our minds are while we're paying no attention to our thoughts, as we shower or eat. A diary can help us become conscious of all these ideas and learn from them."**

If such thoughts do pop up, then turn the paper over and write that negative thought on the back. State the reason why you think that affirmation isn't true: "I'm too sick," or "I don't deserve to get well."

Then return to the positive affirmation and keep on writing. When you're done, read over the negative thoughts. If you've really been honest with yourself, you'll probably discover how you've been blocking your own healing process, or why you've been encouraging sickness instead of wellness to take over your life.

Fighting 'Bad' Thoughts

Now come up with affirmations to help you counteract these negative fears or beliefs. You can write out this new list of affirmations or stick with the original ones if they seem effective. Either way, don't hesitate to change the affirmations as you go along to make them more specific if necessary.

Stick with this procedure for a few days, writing your list a couple of times a day. When you feel you've brought to the surface all your negative thoughts and reasons why the affirmations won't work, you can drop that part, but keep writing out the positive affirmations and adding new ones that come to mind.

"My experience with this process is that whatever I have been affirming often manifests within a matter of a few days or even a few hours," Gawain writes. "And I have usually gotten many valuable insights into my own (negative thought) patterns this way."

In *Creative Visualization*, Gawain also devotes a chapter to the value of journal writing in the healing process. She suggests keeping a 'creative visualization notebook' for recording progress, inspiring thoughts or ideas, positive affirmations of health and healing, dreams and even drawings of how you see your body fighting and defeating the disease or disorder that's troubling you.

Some of the writing she suggests for the workbook to help stimulate the mind-body healing process include:

1. Affirmations. Write down your favorite affirmations. You can list them all on one page, or you might want to make a separate page for each. As you read through your workbook, pause and meditate on each one.

BIOFEEDBACK AND MORE

2. Outflow List. Make a list of all the ways that you can send your energy flowing outward to others around you and the rest of the world in general. These can include not only thoughts of health and healing, but also positive ideas about prosperity, love and affection, appreciation, physical energy and friendship. Keep adding to the list as new ideas come along.

3. Success List. Make a list of all the things you have done successfully – at any time and in all areas of your life, not just your work. Add to the list new successes that come along. The idea is that by acknowledging and praising your successes, you are encouraged to accomplish even more.

4. Appreciation List. Make a list of everything you are thankful for or that you appreciate having in your life. This list heightens your awareness to the riches and blessings all of us often take for granted. It increases your awareness of abundant good health and thus enhances your ability to manifest that blessing in your everyday life.

5. Self-Esteem List. Make a list of all the things you like about yourself. The more you acknowledge your positive qualities, the happier you'll be about yourself and your condition. When you feel good about yourself, your creative energies are unleashed and your inner healing powers soar.

6. Self-Appreciation List. Write down all the ways you think you can increase your pleasure or satisfaction in your life. They can be small gifts to yourself, things you can easily do every day. Then check your list daily and pick out one thing to do to make you feel better about yourself and increase your sense of satisfaction and well-being.

7. Healing and Assistance List. Write down the names of any people you know who need healing or special assistance. Create affirmations for those people and their needs, and write them down. Every time you look through your notebook, pay special attention to these healing affirmations for others, because one of the great truths of the universe is that you really can't give anything away – what you give you get back tenfold.

BIOFEEDBACK AND MORE

8. Creative Ideas. Jot down any ideas, dreams or your wildest fantasies. Build castles in the air and make great plans for the future. Don't worry if they sound crazy or outlandish. By stimulating your creative thinking in this way, you'll strengthen your powers of creative visualization and imagery that are among the greatest healing powers of the mind. "You may find it difficult to take time out of your busy schedule to work in your notebook," Gawain advises. "Yet if you take a few minutes a day, or an hour or two every week or so, you will find that so much work is accomplished on the inner plane, it is often worth a 100 times the amount of time and energy you would have spent on the outer plane."

> **Many doctors and hospitals now 'prescribe' music tapes instead of pain-killers and tranquilizers.**

We've been told for centuries that 'music has charms to sooth the savage breast', but now mind-body researchers are discovering that music really does have the incredible power to help heal the damaged breast, as well.

THE HEALING POWER OF MUSIC

Reports are pouring in from hospitals coast to coast on the amazing way that music seems to inspire and speed the healing process. Music is being used to prepare patients, especially children, for heart catherization and surgery, to help women during childbirth and to help cancer patients cope with chemotherapy. Music therapy is used to ease chronic back pain and spinal injuries. Music and relaxation are combined to treat such stress-related illnesses as high blood pressure, migraine headaches and ulcers.

The Kaiser Permanente Medical Center in Los Angeles has been one of those leading the way in using music as a mind-body healing technique. Patients there now have the option of a prescription or listening to 20 minutes of soothing harp music accompanied by guided relaxation.

Mind-body specialists at the University of Massachusetts

BIOFEEDBACK AND MORE

> In St. Louis, music therapist Nancy Hunt uses music in healing because "Music is a marvelous and extremely powerful tool," she says. "It increases blood volume, decreases and helps stabilize heart rate and lowers blood pressure... It can make us relax, or remember, or to have all sorts of feelings."

Medical Center produced an hour-long music video that guides patients through a mindfulness meditation session.

The video is extraordinarily helpful for patients coping with chronic, excruciating pain. The music is a soothing vehicle that helps patients 'flow' into a deep, healing meditation. Harp music was specifically chosen for the video because the harp has traditionally been an instrument for healing and calming the mind.

Dr. Steve Halpern, a California composer and music-therapy researcher, has produced scores of audio and video tapes to help learn and improve healing meditations and to enhance visualization.

In selecting music to heal by, Halpern suggests that if you breathe deeper and slower as you listen, then you have the right type of music to relax you and help you meditate or visualize. Many of the great pieces of classical music, especially those by Bach or Handel, contain the 60 beats-per-minute that's ideal for synchronizing your heart beat.

Among the recommended classicals are Beethoven's *Fifth Symphony;* Bach's compositions, especially his *Mass in B Minor*; Mozart's *The Vespers*; Schubert's *Ave Maria*; Schumann's *E-Flat Major Symphony*, and Dvorak's *New World Symphony*.

Classical music is beneficial, but so is jazz, blues, popular music, electronic synthesizer, even some rock, as long as you know your body is responding the way you want it to, by either relaxing or becoming energized.

Having the right music for your healing sessions, notes Halpern, is just as important as having the right food and vitamins in your kitchen.

The Ancient Wisdom of MADAME SPIRA'S LIVE Psychic Network

NEW NEW NEW

LOVE, HEALTH & MONEY

PROFESSIONAL PSYCHICS AVAILABLE 24 HOURS A DAY

CALL 1-900-370-7447

$3.99 per minute

Must be over 18. Service not available outside U.S. For entertainment purposes only. Globe Communications, NY, NY

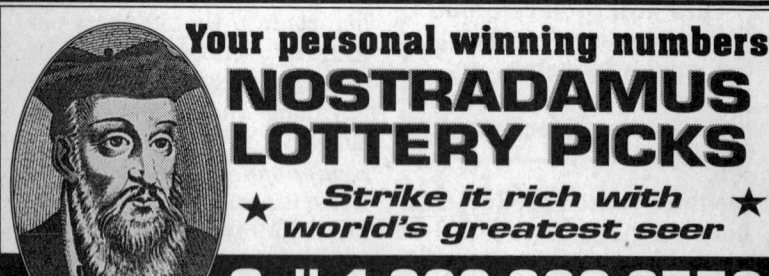

Your personal winning numbers
NOSTRADAMUS LOTTERY PICKS

★ *Strike it rich with world's greatest seer* ★

Call 1-900-820-0770

$1.99 per minute

Must be over 18. Service not available outside U.S. For entertainment purposes only. Not to be used for any form of illegal gambling. Globe Communications, NY, NY.

CALL TODAY!
FIND OUT WHAT THE STARS HOLD FOR YOU
LOVE SUCCESS HEALTH

— PLUS —

UNCOVER THE MYSTERIES OF THE TAROT:
What does the Queen of Wands mean for you?
Will the Two of Cups change your life?

CALL NOW FOR YOUR PERSONAL HOROSCOPE & TAROT READING

1-900-976-6060

$1.99 per minute.

Must be over 18 years old. Not available outside U.S. Touchtone phone required. Sponsored by Globe Communications, NY, NY.